RICHARD, MYRTLE AND I

RICHARD, MYRTLE AND I

BY STEPHEN HUDSON, pseud.

Sydney Schiff

Newly Edited by
Violet Schiff

With a Biographical Note
And a Critical Essay
By Theophilus E. M. Boll

PHILADELPHIA
UNIVERSITY OF PENNSYLVANIA PRESS

© 1962, by The Trustees of the University of Pennsylvania
Published in Great Britain, India, and Pakistan
by the Oxford University Press
London, Bombay, and Karachi

Library of Congress Catalogue Card Number: 62-7201

Printed in the United States of America

. . . He lives for the work that is in him to do while
life-strength lasts . . . .

—From Richard Kurt's tribute to Epstein.

ACKNOWLEDGMENTS

Since no diaries, journals, or personal letters exist to form a basis for a full biography, this first note on the facts of the external life, and this first interpretation of the creative life of Stephen Hudson have been made possible only through the infinite kindness and helpfulness of Stephen Hudson's widow, who so graciously transformed hours of questioning her into delightful visits for tea, and who extended her guidance until my work was completed. Stephen Hudson's sister, Mrs. Rose Morley, and his niece, Mrs. Esmé Cooke, have also been very helpful in supplying me with information and photographs.

My thanks are due to Graham Stainforth, M.A., Master of Wellington College, to the Very Reverend F. T. Nock, Dean and Rector of St. Luke's Cathedral, Sault Ste Marie, Ontario, and to R. E. Clifford, Esq., Head Clerk of the Oxford University Registry, for their kindness in sending me information contained in official records and for making inquiries to supplement the records.

The privilege of meeting Violet Schiff I owe to Professor Albert C. Baugh, who encouraged me to apply to the American Philosophical Society for a grant that sent me to England in the summer of 1959. Professor Mark Longaker read the manuscript of the note and the essay in its early and later forms, and generously gave me the benefit of his stimulating criticism.

The members of the British Museum Reading Room staff extended their typical hospitality and efficiency to me. The family of the University of Pennsylvania Library, in particular Mrs. Alice Cullis, Head of the Acquisitions Department; Miss Lilian Guthrie, Custodian of the Furness Memorial Library;

Mrs. Delphine Richardson, Inter-Library Loan Librarian; Mrs. Neda Westlake, Head of the Rare Book Room; and Mr. Bernard J. Ford, Head of the Circulation Department, have tirelessly given me the enthusiastic, efficient cooperation that marks the *esprit de corps* of the University Library family.

My years of study in the twentieth century English novel have had the generous support of the University's Committee on the Advancement of Research.

I gratefully acknowledge the permission of the Cresset Press to reproduce passages from *The Present Age* and from *The Other Side*; of the Hogarth Press to quote a passage from Edwin Muir's *Autobiography*; of Ernest Benn, Ltd., to quote passages from John Gawsworth's *Ten Contemporaries*; and the good wishes of Alfred A. Knopf, Inc., the first American publishers of Stephen Hudson's works, on this new version of *Richard, Myrtle and I*.

T. E. M. B.

PREFACE

It is my hope that this new edition of a novel that has been well described as "a spiritual autobiography . . . in which every true artist will find some revelation of himself," will reawaken an interest in the genius of Stephen Hudson, and will lead to further explorations of the biographical and critical paths that have been covered over by the leaffalls of time.

Stephen Hudson's contribution to the English novel is a writer's uniquely clear memory of a drama he had been observing and taking part in: the drama of his autonomous generic impulses and a velleity to create being acted upon by chance influences, and evolving at last into an organized individual self. This self, controlling both impulses and influences, recreates in a series of novels the essential meaning of its generically drifting past and the essential meaning of the lives of the few persons into whom it has gained the surest insight. The writer's own life, because he knows it most completely, is his principal source of creation. *A True Story* is the full record of Stephen Hudson's apprenticeship to the creative life, and is related, not too distantly, to *Pendennis*. *Richard, Myrtle and I* concludes the story by describing the climax to apprenticeship, the passage to creation.

The progress toward a realized self was an adventure that Dorothy Richardson understood, a drama that George Gissing, May Sinclair, and J. D. Beresford represented, and a journey on which James Joyce lost his way. Stephen Hudson is second to none in the honesty and lucid art with which he has given reality to his novels of insight into individuation. That he has not so far been given a place in the histories of the English novel should be an invitation to read him rather than an excuse for not reading him. What sort of brave intellectual world is ours if we are content to make do with what historians have had time to set down to date?

T. E. M. B.

CONTENTS

ILLUSTRATIONS

The following illustrations appear as a group after page 64

BIOGRAPHICAL NOTE

STEPHEN HUDSON

(1868-1944)

The wonder a reader of Stephen Hudson's novels feels over that writer's neglect by contemporary historian-critics must turn for its answer to the question of what it is they now ask of the novelist.

First, they give the healthy child's order, "Tell me a story." Next, they pose the mature adult's request, "Show me real people." These have long been the basic demands, lucidity being allied with beauty in an auxiliary role of calibrating the aesthetic satisfaction of the basic demands.

But in this century two further canons have gradually been added to the critical dogma for the recognition of genius. The first is the perfectly understandable infiltration into the requirements of criticism of the surrounding mass-phenomena of applied literacy: the allo-logics of crossword puzzle-solving, the popularity of allographic autobiographies, and that triumph of communication, the scrambled message. Yielding to the suggestions of these, criticism has come to revere a style that will both challenge the reader's powers of decoding and also reassure him that the translation is not exactly determinable. Directness and lucidity have lost their old prestige. The new taste in style for genius shows a preference for the arhetorical, the equivocal, the kaleidoscopic, the free subliminal, and the fabricated symbolic.

The second new canon has been unobtrusively set up by the

absorption of the age in the social man, the natural result of continued advances in industrialization and increases in urbanization and internationalization. It gives the order, "Show us people getting together." That novelist is therefore preferred who dramatizes the insistent interpersonal relationships and patterns their reference to social themes and social theses. The greater emphasis on the social man has been shifting attention away from the sense of responsibility that acts within a person and that induces tension for the drama of the individual life, to expand the concept of social responsibility that acts from without and that produces tensions for a drama between masses of persons. When masses become the units of drama only the leaders receive attention, and the non-leaders become anonymous.

Stephen Hudson does not please the contemporary critics in most of their demands. As a stylist, he used the full range of his critical consciousness. He would have agreed with Gissing that "Self-consciousness makes of life itself a work of art,"[1] and Gissing did not mean subconsciousness. He retained no vestige of tribal awe for the mystifying babbler. He never let his mind slip back into the submental; his sanity was never tempted into subliminal logorrhea, into the neologistic condensations that are recorded for medical students as the classical symptoms, not classical literature, of schizophrenia. While he appreciated the stylistic wonders that might spring out of subliminal wells, he was content to remain above ground for his exploring. He always remained conscious, assured, and lucid. He was without any egotistic sentiment in cutting the foliage of his words down to the flower. Is it possible that the critics who fought so hard, and with such a triumph over tradition, for the freedom of the writer to be subliminal and equivocal, have become too exhausted to grant genius to a writer whose clear consciousness is always in firm command?

Stephen Hudson had many friends and led a rich social life, but he enjoyed people as acutely conscious individuals, not society for its elusive complexity or its intoxicating effect of liberating one from self-consciousness. As a novelist he confined himself to the thorough revelation of one character at a time in his attempt to get at the whole truth and nothing but the truth.

He paid no heed to the child's plea for a story. He did heed the second canon, and in writing for adults he created living people, by showing not so much what they *did*, but what they *were;* not so much *what* they did, but *why*. When Katherine Mansfield was embarrassed to learn that her friend Sydney Schiff was the author of the novel she had been discussing with him, Stephen Hudson said to her, "I beg you to believe that no criticism of it as a novel can hurt me. It has no value for me as that. It has only the value of its truth. That's all I care about so far as the book is concerned."[2] It was his creation of real characters and his mastery of a style that needs no decoding that won him the applause of his contemporaries.

In 1925 Edwin Muir championed Stephen Hudson's right to greatness in an essay that is a classic of critical penetration. He began: "If one were asked what distinguishes Mr. Stephen Hudson's contribution to the literature of our age the reply might be that in his grasp of the motives of action he shows a more complete mastery and a greater sincerity than anyone else." And he ended by finding the high qualities of Stephen Hudson's work "more incontestable than those of any other novelist of our time." Edwin Muir showed that the power of Hudson's character-creating lay in his limiting himself to the elemental necessities of cause and effect.[3] Hudson willingly sacrificed the fantasy whose writing might satisfy some unconscious needs for subliminal expression but would be irrelevant and immaterial to the character he had set out to create. When Muir had to squeeze Hudson into a group picture of the novelists since 1914, he wrote, in *The Present Age* (1939):

> Richard Kurt is one of the most completely described characters in modern fiction, and the series of novels in which he appears, the best three of which are collected in *A True Story,* are a scrupulous criticism of human motives. They are more French than English in their logical selection of detail for a specific end, their exact definition, and a moral temper drawn from experience and governed by intelligence. The basis of the criticism is circumscribed, but it is always coherent and serious, and *A True Story* has a place of its own in contemporary fiction, by virtue of its objectivity, its high moral temper, and an art which conceals art.[4]

Katherine Mansfield praised *Elinor Colhouse.* She saw how expertly Stephen Hudson had balanced the portrait of the innocent Richard against that of the sophisticated Elinor, while at the same time enclosing it within hers: "Of course, all the detail, so fastidious, so satisfying, is beyond praise."[5] A. R. Orage, the editor of *The New Age,* wrote of the same novel, "It is for all ages."[6]

Thomas Mann wrote about *Prince Hempseed:* "It is without doubt one of the best, truest and freshest boy stories in all English literature, and that means a great deal, because England is the classical land of the Boy, and has the best Boys' stories of the world. The history of young Richard Kurt claims kinship with everything that has been achieved in this sphere by the masters of the past in England, and it renews what they have done with every modern means—a thoroughly progressive and understanding psychology."[7]

After reading *A True Story,* Aldous Huxley praised the sensitiveness with which Hudson had shown Richard Kurt's consciousness expanding from childhood to maturity. He admired the miracle of Virginia Peraldi's fascination as a real person: "As a piece of observed, strictly 'behaviourist' psychology, her character is masterly."[8] He praised *The Other Side* for its "extraordinary freshness and youthfulness . . . its remarkable recapture of the spirit of adolescence."[9] Humbert Wolfe reviewed *The Other Side* in *The Sunday Referee*[10] as a book whose continuous opening up of trains of thought in readers made no instant and ephemeral assault to capture wide attention, but would become the intimate of the thoughtful many when time had allowed acquaintanceship to ripen into friendship.

Richard Aldington, unaware of the earlier publication of its parts, reviewed *A True Story* in the light of his erudite knowledge of French literature: "Mr. Hudson has worked with that scrupulous devotion to his art, that respect for the reader's intelligence, which we all honour in Flaubert." He thought it "a strange oversight" that so excellent a book had not been chosen by one of the American book clubs. Its merit lay "in its solid workmanship and still more in the fact that it does enrich one's experience of human life. . . . Above all, I find no trickery in its writing, none of the professional novelist's stunts, which are so irritating."[11]

Somerset Maugham praised *The Other Side* for its exact recapture of the material and spiritual reality of its long past time—1887—and for the reality of the people: "The characters are sharply drawn so that one can see them clearly and they stink of truth. I find myself quite unable to read the book as a novel, I believed it without any reservation and took it for a chapter of your own life, put down with extraordinary skill."[12]

Professor J. Isaacs said in a broadcast on Stephen Hudson,

"Nothing more exciting in modern literature has been seen by those who watched it, than the growth of the Kurt saga."[13]

American critics were just as appreciative. A long review of *Richard, Myrtle and I* in the *New York Times* credited Hudson with "forging a new mode for the novel, and a highly individualized aesthetic of living. . . . His prose style is a supple and graceful instrument which cuts clear and clean to the very heart of matters. He is one of the most brilliantly lucid novelists of ideas." It gave fair warning that the book is alert and vigorous, and "calls for tough-minded collaboration. It will give short shrift to the reader who undertakes to dream over its pages."[14] Louis Kronenberger, reviewing the same novel, said of Stephen Hudson, "No English writer of our generation is so obviously caviar. . . . Substance, texture, form, style—every standard by which a writer can be judged—are in Hudson's case unique things, difficult to grasp except with the whole mind and artistic consciousness. . . . One wonders sometimes whether Hudson is not carrying fiction to a subtler length, and with no less assured a hand, than even James Joyce."[15]

To the great cost of prestige, Stephen Hudson did not support his contemporary critics with those cheerfully offered confidences and those critical philosophizings about his art that the novelist with a good marketing sense naturally indulges in, both to make his personality known, and to prove his seriousness as an artist. The most he would do, when John Gawsworth gave him a chance by asking him to contribute to his *Ten Contemporaries,* was to write an essay that he modestly called "Apology and Extenuation." He wrote:

> . . . The only book that I have written is an unfinished novel. The volumes which have been published are little more than the framework for it. I have for long been living that novel and am still living it.

I have never had any desire to write for the sake of writing and I am devoid of ambition. I have accumulated a quantity of vital experience which remains in a state of flux. Continuously passing in and out of my consciousness it demands to be sorted out and synthesised. When the chaos becomes unbearable I start writing and go on until the congestion is relieved. It does not follow that a book emerges as a result of this more or less painful parturition. Sometimes quite a large number of sheets covered with words are accumulated and amongst the pile of them a few survive. The tattered bulk goes into the dustman's cart.[16]

Tony he shrugged off cruelly:

The book, in my opinion, fails because Tony is too crude a being to sustain the long monologue. His slangy, colloquial idiom becomes monotonous and there is not enough light and shade to relieve the unilateral tension.[17]

We ought not to misunderstand that modesty of his. It was based on a pride that aimed at perfection because nothing lower was worth aiming at. After the labor of creating was over, Hudson measured what he had done against what he judged to be the supremely great; any lower standard meant a concession his pride would not make. And one must not forget that when he published the first book of which he was not ashamed he was already fifty-one. No man is as much an exhibitionist at fifty as he might have been at one-and-twenty.

He was reticent about his private life because he felt that he had told all that mattered about himself in his novels. He lived for his writing, and his books were his truest reality. He may even have been shy over his parents' marital complexities, although his own he bared in his novels. Stephen Hudson's refusal to invite or give interviews, to sentimentalize or heroize himself, has made personal details about him very scarce. He kept no known journals that would assist the biographer, and no letters apart from a few that referred to his books. Yet a beginning must be made, so that the reality of Stephen Hudson as a person can support the enduring reality of his art. I have woven together some of the neutral-colored threads of the warp that must some day take on rich colors to display the life that was of such fine outer texture and so exciting within. Family history, letters, and memories will have to come out of their hiding places to be assembled to give color and animation to the written portrait.

The grandfather of Stephen Hudson, Leopold Schiff, was born in Frankfurt, Germany, and left that city as a young man to make his fortune in the glamorous Italianate seaport of Trieste. I do not know the order of these two events; only that he became a highly successful and esteemed banker there, and married into an Austrian family that had been in Trieste for some generations and that was known, in Trieste fashion, by both German and Italian names: Wohlheim and Boncasa. His portrait, painted in middle life, shows him to have been a man who, though forceful, was neither hard nor self-centered. The lines in his strong face were left by deep thought, sensitiveness, affection, by pleasure in the social and the fine arts.[18]

When Leopold died, his son Alfred George, one of three sons, was not yet twenty. As a member of a highly cultured family Alfred had acquired a perfect command of four languages: the co-racially native Italian and German, the continental French, and, the summit criterion of culture among the elite of Trieste, English. Alfred repeated his father's history by preferring an adventurous to a pedestrian search for fortune and family—in another country. For the climate of his financial and domestic success he chose the land of his cultural summit.

He arrived in London with his inheritance in 1860, and in 1866 was admitted to membership of the London Stock Exchange. In 1878 his brother Ernest followed him onto the Stock Exchange and became his partner, forming the firm of A. G. Schiff & Company.[19] Ernest never married. A second brother, Charles, went still further west, to America, to become a financier and manager of railroads and to marry an American wife.

Alfred was a person of considerable fascination and brilliance, and made his way as easily in London society as in London finance. In repeating his father's wisdom of choosing for his wife a woman whose family had grown deep roots in his adopted land, Alfred introduced the variation of falling in love with an Englishwoman who was already married and the mother of a year-old girl. The beautiful Mrs. John Scott Cavell, born Caroline Mary Ann Eliza Scates into a long-established county family, had received so thorough an education in France that she was often taken to be a native; England had trained her to be splendid as hostess and as horsewoman. It is a pity no letters remain to help us reconstruct out of faded writing the original passion with which the brilliant Jew from Trieste and the county-born Englishwoman loved. The child of their scandalous passion was Sydney Alfred Schiff: Stephen Hudson.

The birthdate and birthplace of Stephen Hudson remain secrets hidden, with Victorian finality in guarding the incognition of the unconventional, somewhere in the grave and in Somerset House, the latter of which offers no help if the inquirer does not know already the exact name in which a birth was registered. Many possibilities of the register, starting with the obvious names of Cavell, Scates, and Schiff, and including the elemental designation "male child" that I traced, did not lead back to an acknowledgement of either parent. A doctor who had spent his professional life on the staff of St.

George's Hospital in London, which repeatedly caught my attention, assured me, when I met him at The Club in Sidmouth, that irregular births were registered in his day in untraceable ways. Stephen Hudson's father told him he had been born in London on December 12, 1868, and the strongest verification of the birthyear is the portrait by Alessandro Ossani, helpfully dated 1874. The very beautiful boy, with golden blond hair, very dark, deeply perceptive and trustful eyes, and richly affectionate lips, indeed looks just six years old.[20]

After Mrs. Cavell was divorced, she married Alfred Schiff on August 14, 1869, in the Register Office in Kensington. He gave his age as twenty-nine, and Caroline gave her age as twenty-five. There were two witnesses, Emma E. Trego and C. R. Rogers Harrison.[21] Mrs. Cavell brought her little girl Louise with her, to give Stephen Hudson an older sister.

Until they were grown up and a maid let out the secret, to the great anger of Mr. Schiff, the children of this marriage did not know that Louise, "Sissy," was not their full sister. Then they were told that their mother had been a widow with a little girl when their father married her, and that story became the official version to be told to the inquiring world. One little detail made the boys curious; they were not told what their mother's name had been before she married their father. All together, there were five children besides Louise: Sydney, Ernest, and the three girls, Edith, Rose, and Marie. Louise was always cool and aloof from the rest; she was wholly English. The others were a strongly temperamental lot, complex, emotional, the offspring of vital parents of contrasting nationalities.

The portrait by Ossani of Alfred Schiff in his thirties is that of a virile-looking, red-cheeked, handsome man, with curly blond hair and a blond beard that gave him the sobriquet of

"Barbarossa," clearly a man whom women would like.[22] The portrait of Mrs. Schiff[23] when she was not yet thirty represents a rather sulky woman, looking about forty, whose expression seems to ask what she was being offered to degrade herself, and whose method of raising the bid was to assume a scornful pose, especially noticeable in the drooping wings of her mouth. Her hard countenance and her very expensive and showy dress reflect her membership in a different world from that in which she lived when she was photographed as a young woman holding her prayer book in her lap, dressed in an elegantly plain dark dress, looking at life with clear, innocent eyes above a mouth whose drooping wings formed a smile as if in prayer. A photograph taken when she was fifty-one is that of a woman of seventy who has suffered severe shocks from fear and pain and grief. The mouth that in the portrait by Ossani had let its lower lip hang voluptuously has drawn the lip back to restore the thin track of mouth in the photograph of the innocent girl; but it is narrower and straight, without wings; the glossy dark hair has turned a gray that is nearly white.

A daughter remembered her as a beautiful woman, adored by her husband and her children. A granddaughter remembered her grandmother's reputation as a *grande dame*, a woman of decisive will and bold presence. Mrs. Schiff was once approaching a barrier gate in Victoria Station when a ticket collector noticed her unique white poodle, Curly, which she was carrying under her arm. Dogs were apparently forbidden in trains at the time. The collector asked her, "Is that a dog, madame?" Mrs. Schiff, sailing briskly through the gate, replied, "No, it's a prince in disguise!" And once the grand manner was turned against her. A fire engine was racing toward a fire when one of its horses collapsed in Regent Street, close to a shop in front of which Mrs. Schiff's carriage and her perfectly matched horses were standing. Displaying a talent quite like hers for rough riddance of an obstacle, the firemen quickly removed the beautiful horses, attached them to their engine in place of the exhausted horse and its mate, and resumed the gallop to the fire, without any known remonstrance from the lady.

Mr. Schiff concentrated on making money for his wife to spend, and Mrs. Schiff managed the lavish entertaining. Their daughter Rose recalled the Open House on Sundays, when musicians, painters, literary people, publishers, and financiers filled the home. Talk about literature and the fine arts was part of the pleasant atmosphere and formed the life-long interests of the girls. Their music they practiced seriously.

Everyone in the family rode. Riding was both an exercise and a fine art for Mrs. Schiff, Sydney, and the girls. Rose explained: "We were all brought up with horses. . . . Sydney was never so happy as with horses."[24]

To his sisters Sydney was a kindly, generous, lovable brother, never speaking malice of anyone, and Rose thought his sense of humor was magnificent. His brother Ernest, two years younger, was the stronger physically, good-looking too, affectionate and generous, but highly sexed, irresponsible, and weak in self-control. Life for the girls was a joyous affair, and they gave the parents they adored no trouble, but Mr. Schiff found his sons troublesome, excessively high-spirited, rebellious against control. He was a strong disciplinarian toward them, but he never understood them, and never learned how to manage them. His orderly business mind was impatient with the childish scrapes they were always getting into, and unsoftened by any memories of foolish episodes of his own childhood in Trieste. He wanted them to go into the firm, but they were work-shy, and resisted the complete surrender of their freedom that would follow their placing themselves under his orders in an office. They wanted to amuse themselves, and they loved spending money to do so. Their mother would have had them enter one of the services, as the men in her family had done, but that alternative discipline did not appeal to them either. Mr. Schiff soon realized that Ernest was too much for him, and concentrated his hopes upon Sydney.

The record of Sydney's education, which included much tutoring, as *Prince Hempseed* informs us, is recoverable now to the extent of only a couple of facts. When he was twelve Sydney went to G. T. Worsley's preparatory school,[25] which was to become Evelyns, at Hillingdon, Uxbridge,[26] and when he was not yet thirteen he entered Wellington College, in Crowthorne, Berkshire, at the beginning of the Summer Term in 1881. The House he was in was then known as Kempthorne's, and the Master was the Rev. E. C. Wickham.[27] Wellington under Dr. Wickham was distinguished by the Master's introducing cricket to replace the rough twenty-players football, competitive examinations to select at least some of the eighty Foundationers, and courteous relationships between the Master and his Sixth Form pupils, like those existing between a don and undergraduates. These changes, from the sterner handling by Dr. Edward White Benson, who expected that his pupils would be boors, infused gentleness and courtesy into a public school that had been founded as a memorial to England's great general and gentleman, the Duke of Wellington.[28] Its founders' intention, that it should educate the sons of officers, must have guided Mrs. Schiff in her choice of a school for her favorite son. Sydney left Wellington at the end of the Summer Term in 1882.

Since Sydney was immovable toward his father's business, Mr. Schiff advanced the substitute hope that he would agree to prepare himself for Oxford, and enroll there to train for a profession, preferably law; and in the summer of 1886, Sydney entered for responsions. He did not pass then, but in September of the same year he tried again, and this time his name appeared in the pass list.[29] Although Sydney thought well of Oxford as the place where he might discover and develop the abilities he felt he had, he was not willing to go on his father's condition that he must prepare for a definite career. He knew it was no use to suggest literature as a career; his father and his Uncle Ernest were of one mind on the utter inanity of that. Ernest's way of passing the death sentence on anything that struck him as being nonsense was the Podsnapism, "That is poetry!" Sydney was to regret for many years his not having gone to Oxford. Not until he won critical success as a novelist did he become reconciled to his having missed a university education.

Certain that he would not be allowed to go to Oxford with freedom of choice, he accepted his father's suggestion that he visit Canada to work on the farming and ranching enterprise of his father's friend, Sir John Pepys Lister-Kaye, and in 1887 went to Alberta. He had become a splendid horseman, and he enjoyed his work in Alberta with horses. The genial society of Sir John and his American wife, who had been Natica Yznaga del Valle of New York, made life very pleasant for the boy of nineteen. When the couple suddenly returned to England, and Sydney was left in charge, the monotony, pointlessness, and loneliness, even in the lovely setting of Alberta, made him restless.

He made up his mind to visit his Uncle Charles, the president of a system of railroads whose head offices were in Cincinnati. Uncle Charles and his wife, who was born in Nashville, Tennessee, were fond of Sydney, and Sydney took a job in his uncle's office. After only a few weeks of it he confessed that he found the office-life of a railroader intolerable. Good-naturedly Uncle Charles advised him to travel about the United States until Sir John got back to Canada, and Sydney acted on the advice.

This was just the time when the mother Sydney loved dearly began to feel great distress from a heart condition that was congenital. She suffered so much from pain and exhaustion that her doctor ordered an end to the strenuous social life of London and prescribed a change to a milder climate. Mr. Schiff quickly found a suitable villa on the Riviera, and from 1888 on the family spent eight months of the year in the neighborhood of Nice, and only four months in London, in Upper Brook Street. In Nice Sydney's mother was even further away from him than she had been in London, and her poor health worried him. It added pressure upon nerves that were fretted by his father's strong will and obvious disappointment in him, by the absence of any reassuring affection, by his loneliness in America, and by his growing apprehension of personal defeat.

Sydney's escape from Uncle Charles's office took him southward to Kentucky. In Louisville he met the belle of the city, Marion Fulton Canine, the daughter of Dr. James F. Canine, a dentist who had been trained at the University of Cincinnati and who was the treasurer of the Kentucky State Dental Association.[30] Sydney's charm and his stories of the luxury of society in England settled her determination to wed the young Englishman who had rich relatives in England and America. Names have a power of suggestion that Shakespeare once underrated. There seems more than chance in the melodious similarity between Sydney's mother's names, Caroline Mary Ann, and the name of the woman who captured Sydney so easily. They eloped, and eventually were married by license in St. Luke's church, now the Cathedral, in Sault Ste Marie, Algoma, Ontario, Canada. The civil registry in Toronto gives only the year 1889 as the date; the church record is more precise, August 29. Sydney, lacking four months of his majority, gave his age as twenty-five; Marion gave her age as twenty-one.[31] Sydney had only a modest allowance to support them. After his marriage, he cabled his parents, who were shocked by the news.

However, when the young people arrived in England in 1890, the family received them in a spirit of forgiveness, and even gave a warm welcome to the beautiful Marion. But Marion soon exposed the hardness of her nature. She had brought with her a fantasy of entering on a command of great wealth, and she was indignant that Sydney had to work in his father's office. She was impatient for the large house, ermine coat, and diamond rings that her imagination had presented to her. She grumbled and nagged, and even antagonized her mother-in-law by making mischief between her and friends of the family.

After Mrs. Schiff suffered several heart attacks from exasperation at Marion's vile behavior, Sydney's parents agreed that they had to put an end to Marion's opportunities for provoking her. The decision caused Sydney's mother a grief that her daughters could see, because Sydney was her favorite child, but her health was truly so precarious that drastic protection had to be given it.

Mr. Schiff settled an allowance upon the couple that gave them the freedom to travel in fashionable style. They visited the United States, and in Cincinnati were hospitably received by Uncle Charles and his American wife. Mrs. Charles Schiff, much younger than her husband, was especially sympathetic toward the young couple whom Sydney's parents would no longer receive. They also roved about the continent, from resort to resort. Sydney did get to visit his mother in Nice, but not frequently, and always alone. He was ground between his sympathy for Marion, whom his mother could no longer tolerate, and worry over his mother's health. He suffered from the clear awareness of the irreparable bungle in which he had involved himself, his wife, and his family.

When Sydney's mother, prematurely enfeebled by her disease, died in 1896 at the age of fifty-two, Sydney and Marion were free to live in Italy. His father bought them a villa at Como and provided the funds to furnish it. Marion's taste made it impeccably attractive, and Sydney's flair for finding and arranging beautiful antiques gave the home an atmosphere of impressive taste. Even there the marriage could not become a union, and life at Como was peaceful only so long as Sydney shut his eyes to Marion's admirers and affairs. She needed always to be amused by ardent men who gave her the illusion of worth. Sydney was miserable over the uselessness of his life and over his weakness in making nothing of it, and he himself had an affair with an Italian girl whose family was friendly with the Schiffs.

The death of Mr. Schiff in 1908 and the distribution of his fortune among the children made Sydney restless again. He was bored with the frivolous life that was Marion's pleasure and his own habit, and so hurt by Marion's mocking his experiments at writing that he decided to leave her. He first settled half his income on her, and then planned a six months' tour of the Continent to travel alone, now a man of forty-one, as once before he had started out at one-and-twenty.

He was still in London in 1909 attending with his sister Edith a performance of "La Bohème" at the Covent Garden Opera House, when Edith saw her married friend Sybil Seligman sitting in her box with her sister Violet Beddington. Edith performed the introduction that led to Sydney's falling in love with Violet at first sight. He told his sisters he now knew that he could never go back to Marion.

In 1910 Marion started proceedings that led to the divorce in 1911. After the divorce was won, Marion became the wife of General Sadleir Jackson. That the rich man may not have been so eager to give her all she wanted to make her happy is

hinted at by Marion's instituting separate proceedings against
Sydney for maintenance[32]—or perhaps she was only greedy.
Some years after her marriage Marion and her husband
separated; he became a racing car driver and was killed during
a race in the South of France. Sydney paid her half his income
until she died. The payments, a heavy sacrifice for him, were
the tangible proof of his tender sense of responsibility toward
the ambitious and greedy woman who had hoped to leap on his
back to ride in a grand parade of luxury and social prominence.

The Beddingtons lived at 21 Hyde Park Square. Violet was
the seventh child of a family of nine born to their mother
before she was thirty.[33] Samuel Beddington had independent
means and enjoyed his family with a patriarch's pride in his
wife and his daughters. Mrs. Beddington, a pupil of Les-
chetizky, was a passionate pianist and considered to be one
of the best amateur pianists in London. Her playing kept the
house ringing for hours every day, and her hospitable nature
made her home a rallying place for musicians. Her great friend
the Venezuelan pianist, Teresa Carreno, took her to hear
Paderewski's London debut on the ninth of May, 1890, and
the two came away in despair because St. James's Hall was
practically empty. Their fears for his success were premature;
Paderewski soon became a famous name and a member of the
Beddingtons' musical circle, which included Tosti, Puccini,
and Charles Salaman, the composer, an uncle of Mrs. Beddington and a friend of Mendelssohn.[34]

All of the Beddington daughters sang. Sybil had a rich
voice; Violet, like Sybil a pupil of Tosti's, had a hauntingly
sweet and sensitive voice of exquisite accuracy of pitch and pure
simplicity of feeling.[35] The parents encouraged the genius of
their girls for music, for literature, and also for the unselfish art
of stimulating and guiding other artists. Three of the sisters
won an order of immortality through the friendship and the

stimulation they gave to the creative genius of others. Ada Leverson established her name as a novelist after winning fame by her loyalty to Oscar Wilde when disgrace and the mob beset him.[36] Sybil Seligman, who created a musical salon like her mother's, devoted herself to helping Puccini after she met and fell in love with him in 1904. She taught him to be less gauche in society, and advised him in many other ways, from choosing the furnishings of his home to the reading of librettos for his operas. She remained his most trusted confidante to the end of his life. Caruso and Scotti were among her constant friends too.[37]

Sydney had started out in a family atmosphere that gave him taste for the arts, for his mother had been a patron of artists. But her health had given out just when, in the normal progress of Sydney's maturing, she would have seen some way of winning for her favorite son the freedom he wanted to develop his talents. Her husband's robust will had its way instead, and Sydney was sent overseas to be exposed to the adventurous environment of an America that was growing rapidly to a giant's strength and brusqueness in finance and commerce. So Sydney had been pushed off the path of his special talents and become exposed to the Philistine tastes that loyalty to his father's society, and then to Marion's, forced upon him. The sensitive, individual, potential artist became lost under habits of conventional frivolities, and under the conformity to the surface respectabilities of a Philistine society. The friends he introduced to his sister Rose even after his separation from Marion were totally unaffiliated with any of the arts. His manhood had been humiliated by Marion's selfishness, hardness, and infidelities. He had no conscious hope of ever finding the woman he could love with pride, or of fulfilling wishes he had once held of writing something of which he could be proud. But when he met Violet, he knew he had found the woman he

wanted and needed. She was living the life which Sydney
had glimpsed and which he hardly dared to dream he might
live. Violet offered it to him as his own with herself.

On the tenth of May, 1911 Sydney Alfred Schiff married
Violet Zillah Beddington. He was forty-two, and she thirty-six.
Violet's mother and two brothers, Sydney's sister Rose Morley,
Violet's singing teacher, Paolo Tosti, and Basil Oxenden were
the witnesses at the Register Office in Paddington.[38] By that
union Sydney Schiff's manhood was restored and his latent
genius was supplied with the will to create and the willingness
to submit to the aesthetic and intellectual disciplines that aimed
at greatness or nothing.

The evolution of Sydney Schiff into Stephen Hudson was
the miracle that could not have occurred without Violet Beddington. The excellent linguistic heritage that Stephen Hudson
obtained from his father, and from his mother too, endowed
him with cultural roots on the continent as well as in England,
and placed him at once among the cultural aristocracy who,
whether they become writers or not, can reach out naturally
and familiarly for an expansion of the spirit by travel on the
continent and through the reading of the contemporary authors
of the continent, French, German, and Italian. As Englishmen,
they assume and absorb English literature as their ordinary
fare, and then they explore continental literatures for refresh-
ment, expansion, and exhilaration of mind and spirit. The
practical business heredity did him no harm. It must have had
something to do with the power and persistence of his industry,
his fastidious attention to detail. The very similar heredity of
Venetian commerce and culture from whose practical expression Isaac D'Israeli also rebelled was no handicap either to
Isaac or to his son Benjamin. But it was Violet who made the
potential actual.

The dominating literary influences upon Stephen Hudson

fall into two widely separated periods. As boy and youth Stephen Hudson read Bulwer, Dickens, and Thackeray, preferring the first two. Of the authors read in this early period, Bulwer left the clearest prints upon his sense of style and mood. It is possible that, like Richard of *Prince Hempseed,* he translated *Le Rouge et le Noir* into English, but he left no comment as to that fact or as to any influence of Stendahl. He did little reading of solid value during his first marriage. After he met Violet Beddington his reading expanded and intensified, and his mind, brought to life by her stimulus, began the formulation of its exact standards of taste. He came to revere Henry James, and to admire the virtuosity of James Joyce, and the wisdom of Freud and Jung. But the master spirit who drove him not only to read and revere, but to write his best was Marcel Proust, whose *Du côté de chez Swann* Violet had found and recommended sometime in 1916.

It is always similarities that open the mind to influence. One wonders what the similarities were that captivated Stephen Hudson. Could one have been the society that Proust described, in which artists mixed with social aristocrats? Was it Swann's being a stock broker's son who broke away from business to be a connoiseur of the arts and of life? Was it Swann's falling in love through the medium of music? Was it Proust's confession of an intense and frustrated love as a child for his mother? Art is a profession of love, writing is an expression of love, an expenditure of capital that must come from somewhere, and its best source is a mother's or a father's love. Did his experience of being baffled as a child and a youth prepare Stephen Hudson to recognise in Marcel Proust a brother in the same exquisite agony of unsatisfied hunger for love from his parents? And did the example of one who had gone on to write despite frustration exert its magic suggestiveness upon Stephen Hudson? Whatever the personal tie may have been, Proust's extraordinarily felt perceptions and fertilely elaborated interpretations of experience made him a supreme joy to Stephen Hudson, and then an incentive and a guide. Proust became the model of those disciplines that Stephen Hudson recognised must be accepted for the fulfilment of the intellectual and aesthetic aims of the novel at its best, the discipline of art for mind and emotions' sake. These aims Stephen Hudson applied within the limits, although not on the highway, of the English novel. Proust had let English literature flow into his imagination. He admitted the power with which *The Mill on the Floss* affected him, and how greatly Ruskin had helped to dispel his frustration by supplying him with purpose. Proust amply repaid his debt to English literature by helping Violet exert a similar influence upon Stephen Hudson. And, in appreciation, Stephen Hudson dedicated his novel *Richard Kurt* to "M. P." before he had met him personally. With every novel Stephen Hudson gained skill in removing the emotional camouflages that covered the pure realities of the experiences of Richard Kurt and in fulfilling the creed that Marcel Proust had set down in a letter to Violet: "L'art est un perpetuel sacrifice du sentiment a la verité."[39]

"Richard Kurt," the happy inspiration of a name for his self-projection, preserved the rhythm of his autonym and made a partial assonance with his given name. When he was writing his publishers about the novel that he had decided to call *Richard Kurt,* his fear of being found out by his family and by his former wife to be the author of a novel that held so faithfully to life led him to adopt the Beddington family's house at 21 Hyde Park Square as his mailing address and the name of the angelic secretary of the Beddingtons, Miss Hudson, as his *nom de poste*. He added the martyr-recalling "Stephen" to complete his pen-name and thereby projected a fictional teller from his self-consciousness into the fictional land of his self-projection.

The lives of Stephen Hudson and his wife were directed inwardly to the fruition of his literary genius and outwardly to the enjoyment of the friends who were drawn by their genius for hospitality. It was never the number that mattered, but the quality of the friends who enjoyed exchanging with the Stephen Hudsons the compound and the compounding of respect and affection that are friendship at its highest. Enrico Caruso, Filippo Marinetti, Marcel Proust, Max Beerbohm, T. S. Eliot, L. H. M. Myers, Richard Aldington, Wyndham Lewis, Somerset Maugham, Edwin Muir, the Sitwells, Aldous Huxley, Katherine Mansfield, were some of their friends. They never lost a friend except by death. In Paris Stephen Hudson played the middleman between two celebrated novelists who did not read each other's works, Proust and Joyce. Violet wrote about the meeting, in *Adam,* and matched Proust in the humor and tact with which she described Proust's politely expressed disgust for Joyce.[40] Stephen Hudson's account of his introducing Katherine Mansfield to his wife is a precious gem of autobiography. With a wonderful sensitivity Stephen Hudson modulated his style to make you feel at first the disturbing excitement that Katherine Mansfield, posing, posing all the time, turned upon males through her urgent need to be seductive; and then to make you feel the calm that Violet, always perceptive, sincere, and real, spread about her to quiet the storm that the feverishly tense actress of feeling had raised.[41]

Edwin Muir's tribute samples the pleasure that the hospitality of the Stephen Hudsons gave to their freinds:

> Sometimes Stephen Hudson (Sydney Schiff) the novelist, came over in his car and took us to his house in Chesham for afternoon tea or dinner. He and his wife Violet were ex-

travagantly kind and considerate, and enjoyed, as if it were a rare treat, the company who came to see them, an unusual thing in a married pair who shared so completely the life they had made between them. They had known Marcel Proust and often spoke of him with tender regard, his habits, his ill-health, and his devoted maid. Their delicate enjoyment of company seemed to me a spiritual gift, though Sydney was reluctant to use such terms. In his long autobiographical novel "A True Story" he pushed his honesty towards himself so far, I have always thought, that he was less than just to himself, an excess of sincerity rare among writers. Those who knew him and his wife, and the exquisite quality of their separate and so closely united lives, will never forget them.[42]

Any one who had read his books would see an action that was of the essence of Stephen Hudson's perfectionism when the tall slender military figure in breeches and leggings stepped up to the hunter that had been led up from the stables and stretched out white-gloved hands to rub them firmly across the horse's flank to test its grooming. There was a household custom too that expressed the nature of the man, a tabu against all obligatory performance of any act that was meant as an expression of feeling. Birthdays and anniversaries were ignored as mere bullies of Time. Gifts and greetings and good wishes were never given to the command of the calendar; they were all preserved as spontaneous expressions of genuine feeling.

He had a brief career as patron of a short-lived London quarterly, *Arts and Letters*, for which he edited one issue in 1919.[43] He encouraged artists whom William Rothenstein called "the more adventurous among the young painters," men like John Currie, Mark Gertler, John Nash, and Wyndham Lewis.[44] He knew Epstein, Guardier-Brzeska, Bomberg, William Roberts, Isaac Rosenberg, and collected the paintings of

Picasso, Wyndham Lewis, Chirico, John Nash, Roberts, and Gertler.[45]

He translated as *In Sight of Chaos,* published in Zurich in 1923, two essays on Dostoevski by Herman Hesse issued under the title *Blick ins Chaos.* After his friend C. K. Scott Moncrieff died, Hudson translated the eighth and final part of Proust's lifework as *Time Regained,* which was published in England in 1931. When the American publishers wished to reserve full liberty to make changes in the text, Hudson refused the contract, and another translator was secured for this volume in America. He expressed his feelings about this translation in an inscription he wrote in John Gawsworth's copy: ". . . This, the only work of mine I know to be worth preserving because it is the interpretation of a masterpiece every word of which was and is precious to me." That was written on June 16, 1941.[46]

There was no one place where writing came easiest to him. He began *Richard Kurt* at Eastbourne in 1911, getting the core of it down then, and wrote most of it later in London. *Elinor Colhouse* and *Prince Hempseed* he wrote in London too, at Cambridge Square. *Tony* he wrote at Torquay, *Myrtle* at Chesham, in Bucks, and *Richard, Myrtle and I* at Cambridge Square. In 1934 he moved into Abinger Manor, on Abinger Common near Dorking in Surrey, and there he wrote *The Other Side.*

Stephen Hudson did not survive the third war of his lifetime. On Sunday the third of August, 1944, ten years to the very day after he had moved to Abinger, at about eight o'clock in the morning, the usual time for church service, a German bomb struck and demolished the Manor, the Cottage, and the church. The services had been delayed that morning, and no one was in the church when it was destroyed. Violet, the only person to be hurt, was struck by a bomb fragment that shattered a vertebra. Stephen Hudson had been suffering from a heart ailment, and on the twenty-ninth of October he succumbed to it at the Sackville Court Hotel in Hove.

T. E. M. B.

CRITICAL ESSAY

In 1913 Stephen Hudson published his first completed novel, *Concessions,* under his actual name, dedicating it "To Violet." After the later, classically disciplined novels had proved his genius, he and his wife disowned the book, and by the strict standards of their partnership they had reason for doing so. Its style is keyed to the romantic rhetoric of Sydney's boyhood favorite, Bulwer Lytton, and its male characters are conceptual rather than real. Yet the management of the complicated physical movements of its people on the continent and in England shows a natural skill for narrative planning, and, of most importance, the story has biographical value as the statement of the problem that Violet Beddington faced in helping Sydney Schiff.

Stephen Hudson had begun writing *Richard Kurt* in 1911, inspired by his wife to search out the truth of his life as the primary materials of his art; then he put the start aside to begin another work. I think he put *Richard Kurt* aside because he was stopped by a strong doubt that he knew what the real truth in him was. To get an answer, he began tunnelling inside himself, with his own method of deep analysis, instead of peering down into the interior from the surface episodes of actuality. He let the results of his probing arrange themselves in the imagery and design of romantic fantasy because his mind, even though it was developing with miraculous rapidity, was not yet ready to exercise, without help, a realistic discipline over expression as well as over probing. Analysis and creation are very separate processes, and their controls over expression may develop independently. In the light of this theory, *Concessions* may be read as a dramatic version of the results of Stephen Hudson's analyzing his personal self into its elements and discovering the distortions inherent in the mirrors for self-judgment that his social milieu had supplied him, and that he had not been able to correct unaided because he had not yet developed a sufficiently strong critical apparatus of culture. The analytic probing had to be undertaken and its results made visible, aesthetically inferior as they are, before Stephen Hudson could obtain the self-knowledge and the social insight that would allow him to go on to the rank of artist. It was appropriate that the model in style for this novel of his literary adolescence should have been unconsciously supplied by the favored novelist of his physical adolescence.

Only two important people from life are projected into the novel: Sydney Schiff and Violet Beddington. Analysis separated three possible selves contained in his personality, and two attitudes he wished Violet to hold toward him.

The first of the selves is named John Cooper-Saunderson. He is something in the English diplomatic service in Italy, an ambitious prig who is swept into marriage by the passion for him of an American girl, Gracie Frowde. The marriage appears to have defeated John's ambition, because Gracie suffers from a nervous disease that can be controlled only by the repeated suggestion therapy of an Italian specialist, and John resigns from the service to give Gracie closer care. Their story reflects the mood, without specifically imitating any of the materials, of Bulwerian romantic psychopathology.

A second character, one who has no sentiment in him that would thwart his ambition, is the painter Douglas Mackenzie. He is a genius and an egotist in caring only for his painting, yet helplessly dependent upon some woman who will give him the physical and psychological supervision that will keep him well and able to paint. Because his ego guards all his energy for his art, and because his creativity stops the moment the protective woman makes any demands upon his emotions through her own need of protection, he has no reserve of emotions left over from the needs of his art to give to others for their sake. He is too gentle to be positively cruel, but he can be cruel in withholding normally expected feeling from a person who feels affection for him.

The third character emerging from the self-analysis carries the story closest to actuality. He is Peter Blake, landowner, gentleman, the son of parents of different nationalities: of an Irish father who has died and a Spanish mother. He falls in love with Douglas Mackenzie's wife Zillah through hearing her sing unseen.

The analyzed elements of the novel are completed by the two women who represent the gemination of Violet Beddington. The first is Madame Cadajos, Peter Blake's widowed mother, a concert pianist, equally intelligent and warm-hearted. The second is Zillah Lopez, who has married the artist Mackenzie to give him the attention he so obviously needs and who after her marriage discovers that her needing some human token of affection from him in return for her devotion ends his painting. She leaves her husband, because her original devotion had been a charity to support his genius for creating beauty, and because her leaving him would allow him to paint again. Her singing has already thrilled Peter Blake into a romantic love for her, and she is ready to give her love to someone who treasures it.

To assure Mackenzie's resuming his painting and to persuade him to divorce Zillah so that she would be able to marry Peter, Peter's mother becomes Mackenzie's mistress. Since she has had her fill of love and also of disappointment, she can give to a fellow artist all the physical care and psychic en-

couragement he may want without expecting any return of
affection. Inside the novel, Zillah recognises how very like
herself is Madame Cadajos in her love of art and in her realistic sympathy with artists. So, after having made his analytic
separations, Stephen Hudson dramatized his union in life with
both the maternal and the uxorial attitudes of Violet by bestowing the mother of Peter Blake upon the egotistic and unloving
painter, and the unappreciated wife of the painter upon the
loving and appreciative Peter Blake.

It is after Zillah has gone to London to await the time when
a French divorce will free her to marry Peter that Peter
shows the cowardice he had absorbed from the conventional
attitudes of society, certainly not from his mother. From a fear
of wagging tongues, he would keep out of Zillah's sight until
her divorce was granted. But Zillah explains to him that his
fear of society would make him desert her during a difficult
time, when she needed companionship and the reassurance of
his love. In this way she stirs up courage in him to do what he
really wanted to do. The marriage that in life handicapped
Stephen Hudson when he met Violet is transferred fictionally
to Zillah; but Peter suffers from his original's fear of social
criticism, which made him reluctant to give up a sense of responsibility for the woman who had never loved him.

Concessions, we may now see, dramatizes the analytic and
the reintegrative stages through which Stephen Hudson passed
in organizing into a concerted creative personality three un-
easily jostling components. One was the creative artist, child-
ishly helpless in his needing the care that only a mother loving
with infinite generosity and total indifference to a return of
affection could give, and paralyzed by any demand for affection that would drain emotional energy from his precious art.
The second was the husband whose yielding to a passionate
love offered by an American had led him into a marriage trap

that would require his sacrificing his career from a sense of having to care for his mentally ill wife. The third was the lover who could give love freely because he had enjoyed an ideal confidence with a loving mother. His exaggerated fear of social reproach alone held him back from a complete mating with the woman he had come to love by hearing her sing. The first and the third components were resolved in the novel; the second was stated without being resolved.

These three components, separated and recognised, were fused into a single living creative artist who would be blessed with the maternal woman to care for him for the sake of his art, who would free himself from a sense of responsibility to a spiritually diseased wife without doing her harm, and who could draw upon the loving mother-figure for such a capital of love as he could expend freely upon his wife and his art.

The harsh judgment of *I* in the complementary novel, *Richard, Myrtle and I*, first version: that *Concessions* reflects Richard's lack of courage to face reality, his proneness to pursue false idealism, and his sentimental worship of artists, is an instance of that unfairly severe self-criticism that Edwin Muir deplored. Granted that it is mediocre by the standards of the Kurt saga, it still reflects both Stephen Hudson's courage in searching out his inner conflicts and his intelligence in tracing out the steps by which he was winning his individuation.

Stephen Hudson differed from the pinnacle-figure Mackenzie in being able to love generously, but he lacked two qualities with which Mackenzie was born: strength to ignore the meanly sentimental, philistine restriction of society that would hinder his self-fulfilment, and the will to create in an original way. The meaning of *Concessions* is the effect upon Sydney Schiff of Violet's bestowing two of the three gifts she was to give him: love and strength of ego. The actual insight, the illumination that he needed before he was ready to accept Violet's third gift, he had to experience alone. *Concessions* is the revelation that came out of his search for a real self. Its sequel, *Richard, Myrtle and I,* is the allegorical revelation of how Violet gave her last gift, the will to create.

The first volume to be issued under the pen name of Stephen Hudson was *War-Time Silhouettes* (1916), a series of seven stories and sketches. It shows a great improvement in fineness of texture, in purity of style, and in the originality with which impressions are driven home.

"Mr. Reiss's Final Grievance" sketches a man of finance as he rocks back and forth between generous and cautious impulses toward his nephew. The effect of the end is a nicely calculated sting of irony. Mr. Reiss has, after a long delay and debate, decided to let Percy off the repayment of a special loan of £50 that Percy had advanced to his captain, who had died in battle; then, to his annoyance, Mr. Reiss receives a telegram announcing that Percy had died in battle. . . . The original in life was Sir Ernest Schiff.

"In the True Interests of the Nation" is a satirical sketch of a war-time politician whose façade was his fortune, and whose preservation of it, when it was on the point of being suddenly toppled, he effected with inspired finesse.

"Bobby," the longest story, is a comedy blending espionage with the enjoyable theme of vengeance upon a snobbish scrounger who is made a fool of by a woman spy. "A War-Victim" is a character sketch in comic irony such as Gissing or Chekhov might have turned.

"Dulce et Decorum" is another Gissing-like story of a literary hack, a worshiper of genius, whose self-neglect and concern for others cause his death. . . . The original was the poet, and art and drama critic Malcolm Salaman, the son of Violet's great-uncle, Charles Salaman, composer and pianist.

Some time during 1916 Violet read Proust's *Du côté de chez Swann* and recommended it to her husband. The self-study that had resulted in the cumbersome first novel had not been wasted. Proust now showed Stephen Hudson how to subordinate his analytic penetration to a compound effect of describing the autonomous surface of life and the author's equally living reflections playing upon the highly polished mirroring surface. Proust also relieved him of the notion that a plot was a necessity. *Richard Kurt,* the first novel bearing the pen-name, was published in 1919 and was dedicated, mysteriously, "To M. P." That the new name was introducing an author of noteworthy stature was instantly recognised by Ada Leverson, who urged the reading of this original book upon her sister Violet.

The narrative theme of this plotless novel is the progress of a sensitive young man with great potentials, an inquiring but undisciplined mind, a healthy virile body, a conscience that tends to punish rather than prohibit, a will that is pitifully weak in resisting the frivolous life that bores him and in failing to stick to any positive goal, as he moves in bursts of impulses to escape from the marriage that is destroying him. The novel ends when he has escaped for the time being, but he has no plan of action for the future. He has merely obeyed another impulse, the instinctive flight home.

An external penetrant author keeps the protagonist as the center of all physical and reflective experience, except for a few moments when he looks back upon the Richard of this period from a plateau of later time. The style of the text and of the speech touches a higher level of pure experience than any Stephen Hudson had yet reached. The field of movement spreads over that range of England and the continent with which he was thoroughly familiar: Lausanne, Brussels, Biarritz, Nice, Taormina, Assisi, Lake Como, and Milan.

The narrative boundaries of *Richard Kurt* subtly reveal two major events that had to precede the emancipation of Richard. The novel opens with the funeral of Richard's mother, when he is twenty-seven and has been married to Elinor for six years, and it closes with the imminence of his father's death. The death of a beloved illusion, and the death of the earliest enemy to his wish for an atmosphere of ideas and of freedom for self-discovery were the necessary antecedents to Richard's ultimately attaining a realistic vision and freedom from his family's and his wife's influence; he lacked the will to free himself.

Richard has failed to mature during the six years of his marriage. His ambition to write has no more momentum than an intermittent velleity. His beautiful, elegantly groomed wife has steadily applied the strength of her sneering to humble his will and his pride, and to strangle his aspirations. She has taken callous advantage of his physical dependency upon her and of his pity for her fancied suffering. Richard is discontented with his life, with its lack of any progress, with the frivoling idlers among whom Elinor is wholly congenial.

His meeting with the Vassar graduate Mary Mackintyre in Taormina causes him to discover an independent self cramped inside his humbly passive body, and rouses his inert velleity for a cultured life to a vaulting energy. His undisciplined mind needs the spur of sustained discussion to concentrate attention, and conversation with Mary routs the narcosis that Elinor has induced in his mind and his will. Mary is the first woman in his life to tell Richard what a tyrant his wife is, and to advise him to break out of his slavery and to learn to stand alone if he wants to amount to anything. He cannot stand alone, but he is ready to break away with Mary's support. Mary's declining to be his partner in the venture for which she has prepared him leaves him with the momentum for rebellion and a new beginning, but without a course of action. Still, Mary has shocked him out of his torpor.

His father's purchasing for him the Villa Aquafonti on Lake Como gives Richard an objective medium for his cultural tastes. He helps Elinor turn the villa and its grounds into a place of distinguished beauty; he even hopes to lay the groundwork there for a new and worthier personality. But creation is for Richard's nature an ultimate, not a self-originating and immediate end. He needs a personal stimulant, a personal incentive outside himself. The enthusiasm for a cultural conversion that Mary Mackintyre had roused, Mary had also disappointed. He feels now an acute hunger for love, a love for flesh and blood, and not now for any intellectual conversion. He wants to say to some woman, "I want love, I want all the tenderness of your heart. I want to give you mine. It's there to give"—but to whom?[1]

His affair with the wildling daughter of a poor aristocratic family, Virginia Peraldi, hustles him into a determination that he knows is mad, to marry her, even though there is nothing of spirit to condone a fiercely animal passion. The only merits to the marriage would be an escape from Elinor and a union with someone who was able to feel genuine passion for him. But Virginia's intense fire would kill as surely as Elinor's intense frost. Virginia's refusing to accept the moral responsibility for her sinning with Richard, her pretending to be asleep during the hours which would have charged her with sin had she admitted awareness and given consent, reveals a dishonesty that turns Richard's passion to disgust. Perhaps her dishonesty offends him the more intolerably because it symbolizes his own feigning of sleep over his moral responsibility to free his chained self. The scenes of Richard's last night with Virginia and his departure for England with his dying father equal the great passages of intensity in our literature.

Character themes thread through the main theme. Richard resents his father's advice to discipline himself, and interprets his father's disappointment as an unforgivable want of sympathy. Richard is both angry at, and afraid of, his father. It is fear that makes Richard defiant toward his father, not in the outright form of assertiveness by contradiction, but in the negative and guilt-determined form of keeping silent. An important character theme that cannot be recognised until all the novels are ranged together to allow contrasts to show up is the effect upon Richard of his having married the discontented, shallow, extravagant, self-centered Elinor. From having been at the age of nineteen (as we see later in *The Other Side*) a young man with modest expectations from life, Richard has absorbed Elinor's greediness and selfishness, so that now he wants a big house or a luxury flat in London, a country place for sport and social entertainment, and a decent income without any condition of having to earn them. Why should he work? His father has a huge income from his brokerage house and gambles recklessly at Monte Carlo, and his mother is extravagant.

There are two scenes of tenderness that suspend hostility between father and son. One follows upon Richard's magnificent run of luck at the Casino that brings him the material wealth his father can respect. The tone of that scene is irony, of course, but Hudson intensifies its effect by showing how the fabulous luck that has won his father's admiration causes Richard to swear off gambling. The second occurs when Richard sees how close to death his father is. Compassion, which hatred had checked so long, unites him to his father. Yet there has never been between them any channel, a common current allowing an exchange of thought. His father's standard of meaning to life is material prosperity. Any other standard, like the degree of the reality or the quality of the consciousness with which one lived, was without meaning to him.

Richard's character is seen by his observer with an objective honesty that holds a perfect horizontal level, never dipping toward either satire or sentiment, steadily eyeing the acutely conscious central self. Richard craves the spiritually valuable, and his undisciplined means of looking for it is the compulsion to live consciously every moment. As he explains to Mary Mackintyre, "What matters most to me . . . is to feel. If it isn't actual knowing, it's a large part of it. And the more conscious you are the more you feel. After that comes expression."[2]

He knows his greatest need. "No woman was any use to him unless she loved him, and he meant to secure love somehow. . . . Love was the only thing in the world that mattered. Accomplishment—pah! Let it go hang!"[3]

Richard puts a high value on truth. "He had at least learnt from life that damaging reality is better than the most lofty sham."[4] And he has learned that spiritual yearnings can have only spiritual satisfactions. He and Elinor make the Villa Aquafonti and its grounds very beautiful, but he finds that "the seeking an objective cure for a subjective malady, the creating of an atmosphere of happiness out of material things, the building of a shrine for the worship of nothingness, was the greatest illusion of all."[5]

The style of *Richard Kurt* creates the effect of beauty with simple means. It is snowing at Aquafonti: "He stood there, peering into the whiteness till his head and shoulders were covered with tiny frosty feathers."[6]

The original of Ada was Hudson's sister Edith. Olivia was his sister Rose. The original of Mrs. Rafferty was a Mrs.

McCreary. Frank Harris was the person in actual life who was drawn as George Ellis.

Elinor Colhouse (1921), Stephen Hudson's boldest confrontation of the past, goes back six years before the opening of *Richard Kurt*. It must have been an organic unit in his imagination, for it was written easily in six weeks. The external story-teller is master of every gesture, glance, and feeling of Elinor, and every thought that relates herself to Richard; only in rare moments does he dart into Richard's sensorium or mind for important supplements. Elinor's alert perceptions, which she often does not understand, tell us that Richard, after he has taken the bait of Elinor's sexual trap and before he is married, guesses her immorality in the past from the hints that her friends the O'Haras drop, but he is so numbed by passion and by his fear of violating the social code of honor toward a seduced woman that he submits to the sacrifice of his decent self.

Stephen Hudson creates Elinor in her flawless physical beauty, her bad temper, her tyranny over her mother, her cool appraisal of every visual and tactile appeal she owns, her earnest efforts to overcome the harshness of her laugh and to control her sensual and materialistic impulses lest Richard take alarm, her pretense of love, and her pitiless attack upon Richard's sentimental sympathy and his weakness of will. The deepest contrast between her character and Richard's, in terms of Richard's ultimate individuation, is her lack of insight into her personal generic chaos. Without insight, an individual self cannot form.

Richard's weak will has gained only two small victories over Elinor: they are to be married under the English flag and in a church; and he withholds the consummation and public acknowledgment of their marriage until Elinor shall have been introduced to his parents.

Touches of delicately lurid irony, resembling those noticable applications of make-up that reveal the natural impulse of some women to be artificial, expose the selfishness of Elinor. After she has finished her love-letter to Richard the night before they are to be married, she innocently rubs out the memory of her seven trials at a term of address, and thinks, "It was wonderful how naturally the words came when one was deeply moved."[7] Later, in a chivalrous trance-state, Richard begs her to promise she will tell him if ever she needs anything. Ever-so-yielding, Elinor kisses him and answers, "I promise."[8]

Yet once he is in Cliftonburg away from Elinor, he thinks over what he has done, and in "The Song of the Wheel," the original poem he sends her, Richard confesses his despair and his wish that he might turn to unfeeling steel to carry the burden of his remorse for a suicidal marriage.

Stephen Hudson's asperity over America's concentration on making money, its preference for amusements that require violent motion, and the indulgence by American males in quantum drinking reflects his yearning for leisure to think and converse seriously.

Stephen Hudson took liberties with the events of actuality as Mrs. Rose Morley recalled them, and with the geographical settings. Cliftonburg was Cincinnati. Richard's meeting Elinor was moved from Louisville, Kentucky, to Manitou in Michigan. However, the marriage did take place under the English flag, in St. Luke's Church, Sault St. Marie, Algoma, Ontario. The fictional Reverend C. Hawke supplies in his name a spur of irony that the occasion allowed the artist. Perhaps a gentler mood, such as that in which revisions of *Richard Kurt* were made, might have found the name of the actual clergyman, The Reverend Frank W. Greene, quite as appropriate.[9]

Prince Hempseed (1923) was dedicated "To the Memory of my Beloved Friend, Marcel Proust, November 18, 1922." It goes back in time to Richard's earliest memories of transportation by pram, and ends with his being carried at the age of eighteen as an unwilling passenger bound for New York on the steamer "Trave." This frame of passive transportation, as will be seen, subtly decorates the portrait with its character motif. The style, which at the opening suggests the unorganized flow of a child speaking, and thereafter advances to a usually normal sentence structure, remains, as does also the comprehension bearing upon its materials, inside the age limit of the memoirist. That Stephen Hudson had more difficulty with this novel than with the previous one is hinted at by the many shifts in the time distance between the teller and the episode. These shifts among recent-past, distant-past, and present-time unsteady the momentum of the memoir, but also give naturalism to the recording without deflecting the narrative course or unduly slackening its dramatic tension.

The all-important intention of Stephen Hudson in going back before the time of Richard's meeting Elinor is to expose to the roots the weakness that made the disastrous marriage possible, the weakness of Richard Kurt's will. The novel demonstrates how languid is Richard's concern over the individuation he does not know how to achieve. Drama is induced out of that theme by the development of tension between Richard's wish to be a unified person—it is too gentle to have the force of will—and the pressures of external events that overcome it. Richard is unhappy in his awareness that he is a divided person. He is usually dissatisfied with what he is doing, and then he lets his wishing escape in another direction than the one in which his body and his overwhelmed velleity are carried. A later novel, *Tony*, was to say explicitly what the dramatic telling implies here: Richard is an innocent who would like to understand and control his feelings and actions. The father who is irritated by his boy's weakness and wishes he could instill in him, or coax him to summon up for himself, a strong will, a definite self-discipline and productive control, only rouses his son's touchy defensive anger. Richard does not understand, but the reader of his memoir can understand, that he hates his father because his father is exposing his feeble will. Richard does not understand that affection motivates his father's pressure on him to discipline himself. Nor does Richard discern what Tony exposes, that the mother whom he loves so much and so despairingly, cannot care for him as deeply as he would have her care.

In this book of innocence Richard describes how beauty fascinates him, and also betrays how unconscious he is of the power of the force that even in a boy responds to the beauty of a woman. He first falls in love with someone other than his mother when he is eleven and he has been brought to Ramsgate to recover from the chicken-pox. A soft-voiced young widow and her two children are lodgers in the same house. He becomes so fond of Mrs. Clovis that he wishes he could stay always in her room, lying in her boy's crib, gazing at her.

He becomes aware of sex for the first time, and then vaguely, in the presence of the abnormal. He is uneasy when he is subjected to the tactics and eccentricities of an older male of deviant desires, and later, a young boy of feminine ways fascinates him against his wish. Intuition warns him that if he gives in to the magnetism of Raikes, he must give up the world in which he has so far been fairly happy.

Of his many tutors he enjoyed best the Jacquelins, in Vevey, because they gave him the most freedom. He passes the responsions, but he is afraid to tell his father that he would enjoy going to Oxford only if he were not expected to become a scholar. He would like at Oxford to meet someone who would tell him what he was good for, or, in time, to find out for himself. He concludes that books have influenced him more than have people like the Governor or Uncle Fred, and suspects that *Misunderstood,* by which he may mean Bulwer's *The Disowned* rather than Florence Montgomery's novel of that name, may have implanted his discontent with his father. He suspects that he is a snob, because he'd like to be rich, handsome, well-born, rather than ugly, poor, and common. He forecasts that he will either never marry, or, if he marries, it won't be because he wants to. "I know I shall never find anyone who will understand me. . . . I think I was born to be solitary."[10] Shrewdly he notices that when he tries to think he always looks back, instead of forward. And, talked by his father into sailing for America, to be tempted into ambition there by the enterprise and industry of American business life, he knows he does not want to go there.

The poetry and the truth that contrive the enchantment of the book lie in the revelations of Richard's character. He loves his beautiful and socially occupied mother; he dislikes his disciplining father and resists engagement in the methodical, industrious, acquisitive life that his father leads. He silently defends himself against his father's charge of indolence by recalling how industrious he is when he is doing the things he likes: hunting, reading, tramping to look for beauty in nature, and translating *Le Rouge et le Noir* into English. Just before it ends, the novel offers hope of a surge of will when Richard, not yet nineteen, grasps hold of the idea that he must weld the obligations that will fall to his lot in life to the will to carry them out. That insight won, he turns back upon himself, passively noticing that his actions and wishes have inherently abnegated each other and are spreading wider and wider apart. He does not press his will, but resigns himself to disaster.

In actuality, St. Vincent's was Worsley's school, and Clive was Wellington College.

Tony (1924) is told in that compact, colloquial memoir style which, already used in *Prince Hempseed*, as indeed in earlier autobiographical novels of adolescence and often in comic novels, was to become after 1940 almost the normal idiom of the serious English novel. It draws the self-portrait of Richard's younger brother, who had been excluded from the earlier volumes of the Kurt saga, noticeably so in *Prince Hempseed*, as if he were never to be acknowledged.

Tony was written, I conjecture, out of its author's realizing how much like his own were the generic elements in his brother's nature, that their common weakness—braced in himself by chivalry—had led to his own humiliation, and that his brother's end might even have been his own but for the mercy of a chance meeting at the opera. Stephen Hudson's judgment upon the novel as a failure should be read, at least experimentally and in part, as an expression of the horror that he felt over its personal application.

Speaking on his deathbed, Tony accuses Richard, to whom the whole novel is addressed, of having left him out of the saga from sheer funk over representing him as he really was. He claims his place in the saga, and announces that he will modify Richard's sentimentalism with his own version of the Richard Kurt story. *Tony* begins at Richard's first trip to America and ends in 1919.

Tony is a species of rogue, clever, sensual, cynical, fully conscious of his actions, but not perceptive, and too protesting over his honesty with himself. His colloquial style is a medium for expressing his insensitivity, his usual unconcern for the welfare of others; his unrestricted pursuit of sensual pleasure; his hatred toward anyone who would not yield to his demands; his contempt toward anyone who was soft and easily taken in; and his hostility toward Richard's cultural joys. Tony's supra-sensual creed is, "All that really matters is to have plenty of money."[11] Yet Tony is not pure scoundrel. He usually hates sentiment, but the love he feels for his son irradiates passages of his confession.

His hardness and selfishness make him congenial with Elinor, but he is also treacherous to her to balance his encouraging her to be callous toward Richard. He introduces Myrtle Vendramin into the Kurt saga. Cynic as he is, he cannot find a flaw in Myrtle. Her immediate and unjudging comprehension of his humanity and her alert laughing sense of humor make him her captive. He draws a dramatic portrait of his Uncle Fred, "The Rock," a very successful speculator on the Stock Exchange. A bachelor, The Rock confines his living space to one room of his luxurious flat; he does not know how to expand, how to enjoy life. After exerting persistent pressures on the social ganglia that are connected with the bestowal of honors, and receiving a knighthood, he behaves like modesty herself surprised. He has no patience with Tony's selfishness, and plans to skip him and make Tony's son his heir.

Tony tells us aspects of Richard's nature it would be difficult for Richard to tell us: his loyalty without self-interest, and, adversely, his having been humbugged into a state of religious fantasy in Italy, by a combination of weakness from the after-effects of typhoid and the spell of a homosexual music-master. The faults he imagines Richard to have are inventions of his limited feelings, as when he accuses Richard of demanding everybody's love before acting generously, and when he declares Richard's love for hunting and for horses was just make-believe. He is surprised by Richard's intense enthusiasm for paintings and literature. He sees how, after having been enslaved to Elinor and obsessed by a fear of breaking away from the unloving wife, Richard is given courage by Myrtle to make the break to manhood, and how he is surrounded by her artistic and literary friends, the favorable climate in which she nurtures his growth. Tony even describes the phenomenon of character fusion that to variable degrees and in different directions occurs in every marriage, with full insight into the direction of that transfusion. He knows that Myrtle's powers of seeing and feeling with a rare freedom from sentimentalism and prejudice are assimilated by Richard, and become his own stimulants to experience and to art, without any lessening of Myrtle's powers. *Richard, Myrtle and I* was to make clear that this was Myrtle's joy.

Tony describes without insight into himself some contrasts with Richard. A woman excites in Tony a primitively sexual response. He confesses his bemusement over the mind-play that enchants Richard and Myrtle with each other: they are always talking, and they talk as if they had not seen each other for an age. At a skating-rink he describes their absurd behavior to Myrtle's niece, Pansy Cane, and Pansy defends them: "She thought talking was the most amusing thing in life. I told her I did too, up to a point. She asked, 'What point?' and then skated away to Myrtle before I had a chance of answering."[12] Even when he appreciates how rare is the relationship between Myrtle and Richard after their marriage, he interprets it with imagery that betrays his limitations. "Really, you lived with her as though she were your mistress more than your wife and that's the only way to live with a woman."[13]

Tony's difference from Richard in being unable to rise above a generic union with a loved woman to a particular union of companionship agrees with another difference that the war exposes. Richard defends the individual humanity of every living being. As before the war he had defended Oscar Wilde from the mob's attack, so later he defends his Uncle Fred's freedom to scorn anti-German propaganda. But war-hysteria devertebrates Tony into an easily shaken jelly of reflex hate.

He knows how Richard suffers from remorse, and shrewdly discerns that Richard's strong conscience rides a very weak will. His conscience did not inhibit him, but only prohibited an action after the act, and then punished him with a feeling of guilt. "Half your life was spent making yourself miserable about what you did during the other half."[14]

Tony admits he is generally a tricky liar, and he knows how to defend his liemanship. "It's something to be a good liar in a world where there's so much competition."[15] But he does not want the son he loves to become a liar too. He knows that his father and his uncle had mistresses, and his mother lovers, and because his intuition, not his perception, causes him to sense that hypocrisy at home had formed his own deceptiveness— of which he casually shrives himself—he decides that his son shall not grow up in the same atmosphere of respectable deceit. He insists upon Cyril meeting his mistress, and upon Cyril being with him at Trixie's flat as often as possible.

Tony, the hater of sentiment, sheds his first and last tears when Richard comes to him after hearing of Cyril's death in battle and kisses him.

Just as Richard could not admit or manifest the most attractive traits of his character without assuming an immodesty that was not in his nature, so Tony is prevented from giving direct evidence of the great charm he must have effused to have been the successful rogue. Only a hint of that charm appears in an illustration of his sense of comedy. Worthy of Wodehouse is Tony's reference to his father's butler in the villa at Nice as "that butler, whose name was Arrow and called himself Harrow, or whose name was Harrow and called himself Arrow."[16] No, he could not announce his charm, but his courage in accepting his due without complaint he could and does express. When a copper miner, the father of a maid who has delighted in conjugal intimacies with Tony, has been forced by gossip to act the role of outraged parent, Tony prepares for death by admitting, "I asked for it."

The basic theme of the Kurt saga supplied the motive for the tragic climax, which is exploded by a simple psychological circuit. After Cyril's death Tony had his son's portrait painted in Cornwall, and it was his custom to sit alone in his room at the inn during certain hours, looking at the painting and holding communion with Cyril, while Trixie kept reverently out of the way. One day Tony found the little maid, Delia, sitting on his bed, spellbound by the picture. Tony sat down beside her, and from then on the feelings the painting had provoked in each found a single channel through which to rush, the painting ignored. *Tony* is a direct contrast to *A True Story*, for Tony's course takes a tragic direction, because a flaw in his intellect or insight causes him to misinterpret his surrender to the chaos of his generic impulses, especially the sexual one, as the assertion of a strong will.

In actuality, Uncle Fred, The Rock, was Sir Ernest Schiff. The Kurt Home for Incurables stands for the Schiff Home of Recovery at Cobham in Surrey. Tony was Sydney's brother Ernest, who was at Eton from the third term in 1884 to the second term in 1885. He married Emmie Borlase in New Zealand.[17] He died in The Grey House, Carbis Bay, Cornwall, in March, 1919, four days after having been beaten and kicked by one Albert Jay Nicholls as the result of such an episode as the book describes.[18] His daughter has written a novel in which her father is recalled as a person of high spirits, charm, and affectionateness. Cyril was Ernest's son Alfred, who was at Wellington College from 1911 to 1912, in the house then called Bevir's and now known as the Benson.[19] He was fourteen when he left Wellington, and he was killed in the war. Helen was Louise Cavell in life, and the George Hayes whom she married was a Dr. Alexander who had a practice in Sittingbourne in Kent and was knighted. After his death Lady Alexander became Mayoress of Faversham. Olivia Kurt was Rose Schiff, and Leslie was Evelyn Morley, her husband, who died in 1928. The Neil Carew whom Elinor married after she divorced Richard was General Sadleir Jackson. Irene Cane was in life Ada Leverson, and Pansy was Ada's daughter Violet, later Mrs. Wyndham, the author of the biography *Madame de Genlis* (1958). Beryl Stone was Sybil Seligman. The painter, Stanford, was John Currie in life.

Now that Stephen Hudson, obeying the law of his mind to look back, had turned into beauty the largely painful materials that had awaited their proper moment for utterance, he was ready to go forward with his story from the time of his renewal. The novel that he created out of the period of his new life is a beautiful love story, *Myrtle* (1925). To emphasize the change that his heroine had made in Richard's life, Stephen Hudson later thought he should have entitled the novel *Enter Myrtle*.

Myrtle, in the design of contrast illustrating the central theme of the Kurt saga, is a heroic character who does not have to struggle for individuation, who has no problem of controlling generic impulses. Stephen Hudson lets *I* explain her in these words: "Myrtle is one of those rare and fortunate beings who are born in a state of equilibrium."[20] She is strong to begin with, and her part in the saga is to be the giver of strength. She *is*, and that is her glory; she does not have to become. She does not excite suspense, but confidence. Since drama comes out of struggle, change and uncertainty, dramatic movement was designed into the portrait by showing the effects Myrtle has had upon nine people, the climactic one, of course, being her effect upon Richard.

Myrtle is structured as a dossier novel in nine parts, which assemble like petals of subtly varied shadings to compose the flower that is their subject. Each of the nine parts, or petals, is the memoir of someone who loves Myrtle, and each is a miracle of distinct characterization through as subtle a control over style as any English novelist has ever achieved.

The first part, "Nanny," is the testimony of the nurse who, when she had been carrying her "little mistake" for six or seven months, was hired to replace the pretty mother who had become embarrassed with her riches when the seventh child was born.

Nanny describes the protection Mr. Vendramin gave Myrtle as he prohibited all pressure of any kind upon "Babs," all teasing or handling of her by others. Only Babs's favorite sister, Sylvia, who was eleven years older, was given the privilege of holding her. Nanny tells of Babs's quiet behavior as a baby, of her quick learning to read and her preferring books over dolls always. Myrtle never lost her temper, and she had an inflexible will that she exerted with a calm certainty that it would never be crossed. She never wanted anything for herself that any one else wanted. In actual life, over seventy years later, the real Myrtle was still corresponding with her Nanny's daughter Florrie, who had married and who was eighty-six in 1960.

"Jane Grey" is told by Mrs. Vendramin's companion. It conjures up the musical atmosphere of the Vendramin home in Sussex Square, and draws firmer lines of the characters of Myrtle, the even-tempered and self-controlled; of Sylvia, who married Hildebrand Moreton, and was soon miserable; and of Mr. Vendramin, who was proud of his daughters but disturbed by the presence of his sons.

Jane Grey explains how Myrtle became Mr. Vendramin's favorite by the chance of having been born soon after his oldest child, his son Philip, died. She had become the consolation that warmed again in her father the tenderness that had been frozen by the shock of his son's death. As an infant, Myrtle, by renewing her father's faith in life, had enacted one of those adumbrations occurring in real life that the artist copies and calls "narrative design."

All the girls who remained at home were singers. Jane Grey thought that Sybil's voice was the finest and richest, and Myrtle's voice the sweetest. . . . In life, Jane Grey was the Miss Hudson, the secretary of the Beddingtons, whose surname Stephen Hudson adopted.

"Sylvia" is addressed to Myrtle, as *Tony* was addressed to Richard. It is the story of Sylvia's marriage and of the sequence of emotional explosions that ended when the mentally erratic Moreton shot himself. It contributes to the main theme Sylvia's love for her sister and praise for Myrtle's supreme gift of understanding. "What is that gift of yours, Babs, that makes you always understand?"[21] "How did you learn to know everyone?"[22] A powerful dramatic novel in miniature, it presents the essentially true happenings of Evelyn Beddington's first marriage and its tragic conclusion.

"Adrian" is told by a very wealthy and money-worshipping businessman, a friend of the Vendramins, whom he regarded as the proudest family he knew. He was twenty-five and Myrtle was fifteen when he met her at his aunt Lisa's. He never forgot her large brown eyes, her long lashes and brilliant complexion,

Sydney Schiff's mother as a young girl (Caroline Scates), or as a young married woman (Mrs. John Scott Cavell). Date is unknown.

Mrs. Alfred G. Schiff, painted by lessandro Ossani in 1873.

Above: Alfred G. Schiff, painted by Alessandro Ossani in 1879.

Mr. Alfred Schiff in 1895.

Mrs. Alfred Schiff in 1895.

Sydney Schiff, painted by Alessandro Ossani in 1874.

Sydney Schiff, with his ponies in Ireland, August, 1899.

Violet Beddington when she was seventeen, painted by Van Den Boss in 1891.

Rose Schiff, taken about 1900. Later Mrs. Evelyn Morley.

Rose Schiff with Evelyn Morley just before their engagement in 1900.

Rose Schiff, taken in 1949.

Edith Schiff, eldest of the three sisters, taken about 1900.

Violet Beddington in 1902.

Stephen Hudson at Glion, where he translated *Le Temps Retrouvé* in 1930.

Stephen Hudson and his wife at Horeham Grange, near Eastbourne, Sussex, summer of 1933.

Abinger Manor, Abinger Common, near Dorking, Surrey. This was Stephen Hudson's country home from August, 1934, until his death.

The gardens at Abinger Manor, designed by Stephen Hudson.

and her independent will. He once thought that he might win her as a wife, until he saw that she had not been really interested; it was her nature to be friendly and kind. He could not understand why Myrtle should prefer older men like her singing-master, Signor Bertola, and the composer of operas, Sir Michael O'Halloran, to such a wealthy catch as himself. . . . The Myrtle of real life remembered having once called with her sister at the flat of Adrian's original, and having asked him a question of importance to herself. "Your flat is very nice. Where do you keep your books?" And the original Adrian answered, "Books! We keep them in the office."

"Marcel" is the most lyrical of the memoirs, the confession of a nineteen year old French student and poet's love for Myrtle whom he met at a health resort in Germany, Gastein, where she was staying with her family and he with his mother. Her singing won his heart.

The two young people engaged in spirited discussions, mainly about poetry and love; he was rhapsodical and intense, she calm and humor-balanced. When Marcel spoke of fairy-tales, Myrtle told him she never cared for them: "I have never liked 'Let us pretend;'" and she shocked him by adding, "I do not care for poetry either." She explained that poetry came to life for her only when it was sung. Marcel did not know how mad it was to try to bully Myrtle into loving him. Still, the lips of the passionate youth had enough discernment to sense truly as they kissed it that her hand was "the emblem of her character, calm, cool, firm."[23]

Marcel, named Rogelet in actual life, was three years older than Myrtle. They met at Kreutznach, and never met again. He did not actually know the Paul Bloch who was to meet Myrtle later as a confidante of Marcel.

"Sir Michael O'Halloran" confesses an elderly man's love for Myrtle. Sir Michael suffers from diabetes, rheumatism, and the tenacious grip of a married woman who has been his mistress for twenty years. His great fame as a composer, Myrtle's interest in music, his long acquaintance with her musical family, and her freedom from any tie of love brought them into a close friendship at Monte Carlo, and to his proposing later on at St. Moritz. He hoped that she would give him for the few years he felt he had left to live, the gift of her stimulating companionship. He would write songs for her to sing, and the savor of life would return for him, if she accepted his love. Myrtle considered the proposal, then gently declined him before moving on to Chiavenna. . . .

The composer of the transparently named *The Beefeaters, Old Japan,* and *The Buccaneers* was in life Sir Arthur Sullivan, and the Lenora who held him so long in her grip and who dreaded and warned him against his friendship with Myrtle was a Mrs. Ronalds. The Myrtle of real life declined the honor from a certainty that her father would never have consented to her marrying a man in his fifties, when she was in her twenties.

"Basil Moriarty," an elegant, good-looking, charming bachelor without a penny, but a favorite of society, appreciated Myrtle's creative, adventuring mind, her freedom from any servility to social pressure, her incorruptible strength of character, her liking him for himself and not for his usefulness to her. Of Myrtle he thought: "A day without an interchange with her is literally wasted because its experiences yield nothing until we've sifted them."[24] Their badinage is a delight. When Myrtle wrote him that their correspondence must cease he answered, in part, "I am perhaps the only young man who has had the strength to be your friend, who has never obtruded upon you the love which must take possession of all men's hearts when they know you."[25]. . . In real life Basil's name was Philip Hennessey.

"Block" is the memoir of a French playwright, Paul Block, who introduces himself to Myrtle as the friend Marcel de Blonay had mentioned to her at Gastein.

The memoir contains extraordinarily enjoyable dialogue representing Block and Myrtle sparring, Block to gain the advantage as her lover, Myrtle to check him without silencing him. Each is brilliant, and the result of their matching wits is a satisfactory draw. Block wants an affair with Myrtle, but no romantic nonsense along with it. Myrtle enjoys herself hugely as she explores the many-chambered playwright, and Block enjoys the involuntary self-exhibition that Myrtle forces upon him by her expert unsealing of his stores of wit. The respect of the brilliant and successful playwright for Myrtle is the sesame that releases the equal vivacity, keenness, and wisdom of Myrtle's mind. Their mutual respect makes them wholly frank with each other. Myrtle explains why she is frank: "I want those whom I care about to see me as I really am."[26]

Block, unsuccessful in persuasion, thinks that Myrtle is wasting her extraordinary capacity to savor life. He is ironic as he deplores her refusal; and yet he is prescient with an artist's insight into her spirit's need: "She's bored to death by every man she knows. What can she have in common with the people she meets? . . . This girl wants things her own way. . . . She understands but she refuses me her sympathy. For whom is she keeping it? For her hero, her ideal, for a man in a book . . ."[27] . . . And he was right. The man in a book was to be Richard Kurt. And Paul Block in actual life was the playwright Henri Bernstein.

"Kurt" is the climactic memoir. Even by itself it is a deeply moving love story. It recreates in a distillation of pure experience Richard's becoming aware, through meeting Myrtle, of the abjectness to which his spirit has been lowered in his twenty years of marriage. It creates the recovery of his will to strive, the restoration of firmness and manhood to his limp rag of self through Myrtle's uplifting confidence in him. Richard would have gone on hovering about Elinor to protect her out of pity and an illusionary sense of guilt that he had ruined her life, for Elinor had so thoroughly humbled his spirit that she had even inflicted upon him a reversed identification, that made him project his own spiritual wreckage to her, and made him feel responsible for it and for her. Myrtle's firm will bolsters him to make the break he wished to make, to save himself.

This section of the novel is the only part of the Kurt saga in which a character reappears from *Concessions,* the pianist Cadajos, who is a friend of Miss Vendramin. Mr. Vendramin appears again as the watchful, unjealous protector of his womenfolk. He surrounds them with love and care, without restraining or confining them. Richard says of him: "I have never seen an old face with so much love in it,"[28] and observes that Myrtle's will is her father's law, and that she exercises it almost unconsciously, just barely enough to gain her end without pressure.

When we step back from our view of each segment to survey the whole novel, we recall the passages of wisdom that made us stop in our reading. Sir Michael O'Halloran wrote: "All men are fools. Weak. All artists are weak, the best are the weakest. Of all chains, the hardest to break is the one which binds a single man to a married woman."[29]

Basil Moriarty was being amusing but also wise when he wrote, "No master who loves his art can afford many pupils."[30]

Jane Grey quoted Mr. Vendramin as warning Myrtle, "When you marry, darling, never trust a woman, not even your sister."[31] Sylvia records the painter Ramon Mattos saying, "Women always love those who despise their love."[32] And Richard writes, "I once thought beauty compensated for everything. I found on the contrary it made life unbearable."[33]

A figure of poetry that is like a glare of lightning on a truth that strikes panic is spoken by Sylvia when she epitomises her temperament: "It's my nature to go blind at times, to drink up every drop of the moment and then suddenly to look into the jug and find it empty."[34]

The main theme of *Richard, Myrtle and I* (1926) is the evolution of Stephen Hudson as novelist. Its direct story fills in some of the gaps in the Kurt saga, between the time of Elinor's starting her action for divorce and Richard's completing his second novel, *Richard Kurt*. Its mood is a blend of realism and allegory.

The memoirist, the *I* of the title, is not a simple figure, but an allegorical compound. One phase of the compound is an impersonal particle of will that has been split off from the life force with the mission of finding as a host a likely creative artist whose potential abilities it will drive into creating. It obeys the life force blindly and is a complete tyro as it begins its mission, for it must learn from the beginning how to manage the individual whom it has picked as its artistic lodging and fabricant; indeed, it must learn how to be retained by a host who can be so hostile at times as Richard. Of himself, Richard has only a bare and fickle velleity toward literary creation and a still weaker ego to act the aggressive artist. This *I* can hold only a brief tenancy of Richard's mind while Elinor is about. Another element is gifted with literary creation independently of Richard. It writes a sonnet without Richard's knowing about it until *I* reads it to him.

There is a manifestation of *I* that stimulates Richard's aggressiveness, supplying him with cogent reasons for eradicating the powerful inhibitive forces of his sentimental nature and his respectable upbringing. It is this *I* that urges Richard to take Virginia Peraldi as she feigns sleep, that analyzes her as not an innocent maid, but a woman who wants Richard's passion without committing her will to an act of sin which she would have to confess. The motive of this *I* is to break the hold of Elinor's will upon Richard.

It is also a critical awareness that protests to Richard against Myrtle's assuming during Elinor's divorce proceedings the close vigilance over his moral flabbiness which she knows he requires to remain vertebrate. It turns as well upon Richard, to ask in wonderment how Myrtle can elevate into an ideal the love of a man who has proved himself unworthy of her by offering her a love that is a selfish flight from reality.

It becomes a student of philosophy and of the novel, and when Myrtle introduces Proust to it, it is converted to his fresh, untraditional art.

I is finally a spokesman of widely ranging ideas that could be assembled into a philosophy of life and history, and of the relationships between history, life, and literary art. It sustains in Richard, who is depressed to despair by the folly of the war, some hope that common sense will survive and normal life emerge again after madness has run its course. It satirizes the contradictory conclusions of all the philosophers who have found *the truth,* and calls for an end to ethical judgments that might befog a person's own view of truth. "A man is answerable only to his own integrity, to nothing else. He fixes his standard for himself."[35]

In all but one of its various forms, that of the independent

creative artist—and this was removed from the final version—
I is pure intellect and pure intelligence. It confesses having no
sensory or emotional experience nor the memory of either. This
admitted lack is its reason for being dependent on Myrtle as
the emotional stimulant to Richard, and upon Richard's well
of experiences and emotions for its water of life. It aims to
make Richard want to write, and to impose on him such a
discipline over his sentimental tendencies and upbringing as
will prevent him from frittering away emotions that could gain
immortality as literature. It disciplines him with the dogma
that he must feel a genuine interest in the character growing
into a creation, and that he must press his craft beyond mere
seeming and behaving to the essence of reality. It imbues him
with the toughmindedness to fight for the recognition of what
he has created, and an egoism that will make no concessions
to the connoisseurs of the arts but those which he demands of
himself: the lucidity, the conciseness, and the relevancy that
are good form in the art of the novel.

I makes the decisions of technique: such as, that Richard concentrate separately on portraits of Elinor, Tony, and Myrtle and
that he adopt the external penetrant mode toward the first, the
memoir for the second, and the dossier of memoirs for *Myrtle*.

The unallegorical part of the narrative, with its supporting
analysis, shows how Richard had sentimentalized Elinor's
beauty as a signal of spirit, and his lust as a commitment of
his honor. Sheer sentiment made him believe he was putting
honor above lust, while in reality he was raising lust above
honor in betraying his possible unique self, the self that wished
to become an artist and that was equipped with all the talents
of its calling except an intellectual discipline and the will to
create.

There are three major conflicts that are recurrently sustained,
not successively presented. One is the conflict within Richard

over whether or not love may be sufficient to make life fully satisfying. It is stated dramatically when Richard asks, "I think love is much more important than Art, don't you darling?"— and Myrtle does not answer him.[36]

The second conflict pits the adopted creative will against Richard's system of reacting sentimentally, and only sentimentally, towards himself and towards his friends, the associates and bearers of associations that have no value for his creativity. Richard wonders if the empowering of an exclusive and aggressive ego to win him recognition, if the sharp limiting of his accessibility to friends whose sentimental demands upon his emotions might drain the essential energy for his art, are not wrong in one who is so uncertain as he is of his true self.

The third conflict is over the direction and the content of Richard's writing. Richard's personal gravity pulls him towards the past. The creative will wants Richard to have the forward view, to forget the past. Myrtle has found life so adventurous every moment that her eyes are always scanning the rapidly moving present and her mind is moving with it towards the future. Her momentum meeting Richard's stagnation shocks him at first into motion—the break from Elinor. But his mind continues to suffer from the "Drang backwards" to his parental and his marital despotisms, which joined in causing the essential misery of deep unreturned affection.

All three conflicts are resolved. Richard recognises that Myrtle's love, in spite of its devotion to his happiness, even to the extent of preserving his sentimental friendships, cannot remain satisfied forever with affectional outflow. It is not content to be self-dissipating. It longs to be self-perpetuating. There is an ardent, but not an egocentric will toward creativity in her love that needs another person to fulfill itself, another genius, another mind. Myrtle has such an abundance of love and creative will that she cannot store it all in herself; she needs a creative fulfilment. This need Richard eventually understands and subscribes to.

Richard further admits that his sentimental distractibility needs the management of Myrtle's disciplined intellect, which gives him a center of organization for his life and direction to his art.

And finally, on their side, Myrtle and the creative will grant that Richard must be allowed to reach into his memory, to sever, shape, and project his obsessive past before he can draw upon his new life beginning with Myrtle.

The plot describing the relationship of Richard to the complicated *I* is simple. It starts with *I*'s determining to dominate Richard as tyrannously as his ego dominated Douglas Mackenzie in *Concessions*. It does not realize at first how consummately Richard has absorbed Elinor, how deep is his unconscious love for her, and how destructive assimilating her has been to his self-confidence and his fertility. It ends with *I*'s retreating to the position of being a partner in the "triune consortium," because it has realized that Richard cannot be directly stimulated to will to write. He needs to be inspired by a woman's love, to be occupied by that rare woman's superabundant intellect, and to be sustained by her parallel need for an agent through whom her other-centered creativity can act.

Richard's choice of the realistic novel is fixed by Myrtle's devotion to it. She believes that the novel is the finest form of literature, and that realism, meaning the most truthful representation of life, is the highest aim of the novel. For her, the artist's vision and its translation into the substance of a view are what matter. For both Richard and Myrtle, Proust was the perfect master of that metamorphosis and became, after only one experiment with a largely romantic novel, the source of Richard's creed to hold strictly to the experienced vision. Richard does not have in himself the physical and psychic staying powers to carry a novel from the will to write all the way to the finished creation. These Myrtle supplies by possessing him as creatively as Elinor had possessed him sterilely.

Beyond the story and its analysis of the mystery of creative writing are premiums of empirical philosophy. *I* asks, "If a man is not greater than his love, what has he left to offer to the woman who accepts it?"[37] It discriminates between culture and civilization, and believes that culture is antithetic to modern civilization, that humanity as a whole has never cared a button about culture. "The paths of civilization and culture diverged when the bourgeois supplanted the aristocrat. I doubt if a cultured civilization can exist without some form of slavery." And again, "If a man really loves culture, he must be prepared to die for it like Socrates, only not so pleasantly."[38]

Wittily *I* challenges the Anglo-Irish don who objects to the phallus worship of a sculptor whom Richard admires: "You don't object to that part of the human anatomy being represented dormant. What you object to is its being represented in a state of vitality. Now why?"[39]

In actual life, the sculptor who is a friend of Richard was Epstein, the poet whom he symbolized as a mystical beast was Oscar Wilde, and the critic who was a friend of the poet was Robert Ross. The Irish poet-philosopher-don with whom Richard had an argument about the representation of the phallus was the cultured and charming Fredrick Herbert Trench. The Jamesian-Europeanized-American was Remsen Whitehouse, and Adolph a young man whom he met by Lake Geneva on the verge of suicide, befriended, and hired as his secretary. The mental therapist, Boiton, was Coué. The Irish painter who killed his mistress and himself was John Currie, and Meg was Dolly in actual life. The Galician Jew whose mother was his favorite model was the painter Mark Gertler. The Connemara Kelt was probably James Pryde, the brother-in-law of another painter, William Nicholson. The Eugene Hartmann who prophesied the World War was Eugene Kuhlmann, the historian, and the super-journalist was probably Northcliffe. There was an outbreak of cholera in Venice while the real Myrtle and Richard were honeymooning there, the same outbreak that inspired Thomas Mann's *Todt in Venedig.*

Céleste and other Sketches, published in 1930, is a collection of six stories and sketches that had appeared in American little magazines between 1920 and 1925. All are exquisitely turned and of fine texture.

"Céleste," the memoir of Proust's maid, breathes adoration for the master in its account of his dying weeks and his death. It joins the Kurt saga through the maid's telling how the master regarded the Kurts as his best friends because they were the latest ones and did not strain him with the compulsive ties of old memories and old friendships.

"Sunrise in Conegliano" amplifies the account in *Tony* of Richard's typhoid with the memory of how it felt to wake up deaf.

"'Southern Women" is a delicate pastel set in Nashville, Tennessee, of place- and of woman-worship by a boy. "Frau Karl Druschki" is a brilliant intuitive look into the heart of a woman who needs to be loved but who does not love her husband. "Transmutations" is a perfect short story convoluted to a psychological design. It describes how a husband's fury toward a guest who had taken his wife during a drinking party is converted into an appeasing lust for the man's married sister.

"Sounds" builds its Proustian effect through a series of associations that are called up by tappings of a window blind.

In a letter to his friend Professor Isaacs, Stephen Hudson explained what he hoped the writing of *Richard, Myrtle and I* would do for him: it was "to free me for what I have still to do, to enable me to express myself with greater freedom than I have been able to do up to the present, and to speak out of my consciousness of *now*."[40] It was to put an end to the obsessive memories of the anguish he had suffered in the parental and marital hells from which he had been released, to free him for further progress along the course of his new life. But he did not reckon with the possibility that when anguish had been as deep as was his, the memory of it might be insatiably piquant to the creative palate. And, besides, there was one torment he had not as yet described, whose "congestion" had not yet been relieved: the torment of the business life. Reviving that as Richard Kurt's experience in the picturesque setting of an Ohio railway center in 1887, climaxing it with the most heroic act of Richard's life, his helping a fellow sufferer escape from the law, and ending it by having Richard leave America and so avoid, temporarily, the Dangerous Corner that would have landed him at once in Elinor's arms, Stephen Hudson wrote a book that defied his conscious will: *The Other Side* (1937). In time it immediately follows *Prince Hempseed* and precedes *Elinor Colhouse*.

An appropriate sub-title for this memoir would be "The Innocent Restive." It draws Richard in his nineteenth year as he works in the office of his uncle's interlocking railway companies in Cliftonburg, Ohio, and as he rebels against the mechanisation that business routine inflicts upon his urge to live with feeling.

An ache is linked like a Siamese twin to his unreturned love for his mother, his smart, socially popular, always elusive mother. Balancing the endured ache is Richard's bristling resentment against his father's wish to determine his future. Even at nineteen Richard has the artist's curiosity to discover the constitution of his own mysterious self before he will decide in what direction that self should move. His father's terminal reality is money, and his plan for Richard requires his son's disciplining his body and mind towards making money. Fighting for the freedom to make an inward exploration and self-discovery first, Richard denies the imposed reality of money-making, and after a trial of it, rejects the soul-sealing machine that he feels business would be to him. Richard knows that his soul has only one test for reality: feeling. That is why he craves experience that nourishes his feelings, and why he sees people almost solely as they feel. Business suppresses feeling, and therefore destroys reality. Love and friendship are the great creators of feeling, and of reality.

His thwarted love for his mother seeks out makeshifts to distract it from its twin, the heart-ache. An ideal substitute that is for a time even stronger than his real love is his devotion to a couple he meets in New Orleans; they are Proctor Johnson, the promoter, whose wife is insane, and Johnson's mistress Cora Marshall. And he finds a brief sexual substitute in Cliftonburg in an affair with a prostitute who at their first meeting plays a mother's role when she advises him to get his hair cut. When the treasurer of two of the interlocking railway companies, Leopold Taube, a sensitive, educated German who is dying of cultural inanition, is drawn into an embezzlement scheme that is found out, Richard helps him slip out of the country and, aptly to his own longing, to return to his mother in Germany. And Richard's Uncle Theo, to prevent the newspapers getting hold of juicy scandal about the nephew of the president having helped the embezzling treasurer to elude the law, sends Richard home to England, with commendation for his work in the hated office. Richard returns as undecided about his future as when he left. His sexual experience with Pearl, the prostitute, has aggravated his restiveness and his vulnerability to the next woman who might promise an assuagement of his thwarted love. The Kurt saga came to an end with this last reaching back into Richard's youth, with its last explanation of how he came to be trapped so easily by an experienced huntress.

The style of the novel reaches an ultimate effect of a naturalness that is perfect sincerity mated with perfect execution. Richard tells of his feelings when he met Pearl for the second time at Klinger's beer-garden: "The inside me kept on warning me not to be trapped, but the other had his way."[41]

There are passages that create experience with the purity and sweetness of delicate music. The loveliest of these have as their notation the utterances of faces, that constant challenge to the poetic genius of the novelist. Richard is at Chez Antoine in New Orleans when he observes the vulgar Mrs. Murphy snubbing his substitute idol, Cora Marshall. Richard is silently incensed at the cruelty of the snub. He reads Cora's glance of gratitude to him for his loyalty, the look of loving affirmation that she begs from Proctor Johnson with her appealing gaze, and Johnson's look of thanks for Richard's silent vow of loyalty to them. Strong feelings have flashed between them without words, and have refined the relationship of the three to an exquisitely intimate communion.

The term "exquisite" can always be applied to Stephen Hudson's method of fastidious style-weaving, but it is only one of his many aesthetic effects. His ear does not sentimentalize the inflections and vocabulary of the prostitute as she brushes away Richard's respectful tribute to her humanity. He has told her he would like to talk to her, to get to know her. "Talk," she asks. "What fur? . . . There ant nuthen to know. I'se jest a gurl. S'you a man—? Or isn't you?"[42]

His memory recalls in an unpoetic mood the continuous thunder throbbing on New York's Broadway from the steel hawsers that ran underground to pull the cars, and the penetrating clangs with which the motormen proclaimed their right of way.

Richard writes of his praying at bedtime for his family. "It's become such a habit that I do it mechanically before going to sleep." It makes him think of his mother at least once every twenty-four hours. "I expect I shall give it up sooner or later. When I do it will be because I don't believe in anything. I don't see how one can know right from wrong if one doesn't believe in God."[43]

Some names and places of actuality are disguised, others are retained. Cliftonburg was Cincinnati. Uncle Theo was Charles Schiff, and the initials of the interlocking companies as they are arranged in a column in chapter four represent companies of which Charles Schiff was president in 1887. C.S., at the head of the column, represents not only his initials but those of a holding company, the Cincinnati Southern. The initials below stand for the Cincinnati, New Orleans and Texas Pacific; the Alabama, Great Southern; the Vicksburg, Shreveport and Pacific; and the New Orleans and Northeastern companies. Omitted were the initials of another company Charles Schiff headed, the Vicksburg and Meridian, which had the low net earnings of 5.48 per cent and $29,124.49. (In 1888 that company's earnings were up to 22.7 per cent and $124,-347.) The total line trackage, without sidings, of all five companies in 1887 was over eleven hundred miles, the total assets were over fifty-four million dollars, and the net earnings were over a million and a half dollars. The earnings of the companies other than the Vicksburg and Meridian varied from a net of 18.66 per cent and $90,454 (the Vicksburg Shreveport and Pacific), to 39.07 per cent and $1,124,726 (the Cincinnati, New Orleans and Texas Pacific). The general manager in the novel is Galt; in actuality his name was spelled Gault.[44] Denza was the singing master who really took the original Richard to Pagani's restaurant in Great Portland Street, where the cartoonist of Vanity Fair, Pellegrini, and the composer Signor Tosti were to be seen dining. In life Richard did hear Signor Tosti, Myrtle's singing teacher, play and sing his song "Ideale" in his studio on the day it was finished.

I have put most emphasis on the characters and made only passing references to the style, and I think I am following Stephen Hudson's interest in doing so, but I need to add a comment on the style, for it underwent an important change in purpose.

In *Richard Kurt* Stephen Hudson aimed at lucidity with beauty and struck the center of his target without concealing himself as the marksman; the lucidity and the beauty are the traits of the author openly shaping his material. But from the beginning of his second novel in the Kurt saga, Hudson adopted a new principle of style: the created character should as far as possible be its only source. Style and its extension and massing that are known as form ought really to be identified with character, and the tone, idiom, and rhythm that transpire through the form should suggest the traits of the created, not of the creator.

The style of *Elinor Colhouse* derives from Elinor's idiom; her alert self-awareness; her concentrated attention on externals such as her clothes, her skin, her expressions; her coldly measuring thrift with meanly directed emotions; and her auxiliary production of a kindly light that will blur her introspection and lead others far astray. Turn to the passage that follows Elinor's writing a love letter to Richard on the night before they are to be married:

She read it over. It was wonderful how naturally the words came when one was deeply moved. She put the note in its

envelope, addressed it and laid it on the dressing table. It was
only half-past ten and Julia would be there in a few minutes,
the bars closed early in Wisconsin. She began undressing,
thinking hard. There would be plenty to talk over with Julia;
she was pretty cute. She laid her skirt and blouse carefully on
a chair and took down her hair. It wasn't very long, but it was
thick, and black as jet. She combed it out and twisted it, holding it beside her face. She had much rather have been fair but
how her hair showed up her skin and the natural colour in her
cheeks; her skin was as smooth as velvet, the colour of rich
cream. She sat down and examined herself with the hand
mirror. Her nose certainly was beautiful, so were her ears, like
little shells close against her head. It was a pity her hair was so
stiff, it was difficult to get it to go properly in the nape of the
neck, those short hairs were so tiresome and straight, and curl-
ing them made them worse. She laid the mirror down, undid
her corset, threw it on the bed, sat in her chemise only and
took the mirror in her hand again. The line of her neck and
shoulders was perfect. She let her chemise drop and slipped
on her lacy nightdress, open low in front, with blue ribbons
to fasten it, which she tied with quick skill into impeccable
bows, flattening out the ends.[45]

"Impeccable" is the only flaw, the word that slipped in because
it was what others said of the original when they rated her
skill in perfecting externals. Against that, notice that there
is not a breath of satirical innuendo anywhere in the ascriptive
phrasing of this portrait of a woman whose original was so
destructive to her creator. Stephen Hudson had assimilated
her, and he released her to let her recreate herself.

The memoir style of *Tony* gives us Tony's elemental range
of emotions, his selfishness, his insensitivity, the jaunty brash-
ness with which he gives away his indiscipline and which also
attempts to camouflage his pitiful inadequacy to understand the
life of the spirit, to draw breath for long in an atmosphere of

gentleness and culture. Tony is Elinor's counterpart in self-interest, and it is to her he refers in the following passage addressed, as is the whole memoir, to Richard:

How many years did it take you to learn something about girls? I was nineteen and you were twenty-two and married over a year. You ought to have learnt something by then. It was some time while we were at Dieppe she told me all about your early married life at New Orleans and how you wanted to fight a duel with an old Southern General because he put his hand on her knee. Oh, crikey cockalorum! We got on to the subject of Uncle Fred after that, she was as keen as mustard to know all about him. The Lord knows what you'd told her about him, but anyhow she knew he was one to get the right side of, that he'd got the stuff. I did my best to put her on and when he came over that next Saturday, he was all over her as I told her he would be. She got him placed all right after that.[46]

Richard's development through adolescence is carefully modulated in *Prince Hempseed*. There could not be a more perfect concord of style with social drama than Stephen Hudson executed in *The Other Side*, and the portrayal of the social drama of the book is a far greater test of the writer's power over style than is the presentation of the psychological drama. Richard at nineteen, fresh from years of tutoring, exquisitely trained in the niceties of two languages, the translation of *Le Rouge et le Noir* not long behind him, finds himself assaulted by the oral and visual cultures of an emphatically assertive America. Somerset Maugham, never lavish with praise, paid a tribute to *The Other Side* that was well deserved, for Richard, the sensitive linguist and curious student, comes through the portrait without a trace of Stephen Hudson writing fifty years later. I have chosen a passage that does not dramatize the more obvious auditory clash through idiom, but isolates the visual channel of the social drama. Richard is in New York City.

I took the Elevated Railway, which runs along a sort of continuous trestle about the height of the first floor of the houses. It goes for miles, right out into the country, a man I sat by told me. It doesn't look very solidly constructed and one wonders what would happen if there were a smash. The trains go at such a tremendous pace that you can't see anything, and it makes as much noise as our Underground.

I got out at Central Park, which I wanted to see. Instead of wide stretches of turf, shady trees, shrubs, flowers and a lake like the Serpentine with swans, waterfowl and boats, imagine an expanse of bare dusty ground and a few stunted trees. It looked completely neglected; litter was lying about everywhere and the seats were too dirty for anyone to sit on, except the tramps I saw there. It was worth going further to see the trotting horses racing along a splendid wide road called Riverside Drive especially reserved for them, pairs in light four-wheeled buggies and single horses in two-wheeled buggies and sulkies. I saw several English dog-carts with high steppers and two or three phaetons almost as smartly turned out as mother's but the grooms had moustaches. I wished I had more time to watch them, but Tim had told me on no account to miss seeing Commodore Vanderbilt's marble palace on Fifth Avenue, the Fifth Avenue Hotel, the Hoffman House Saloon and then to go and have a free lunch at the Brunswick Bar. There were half a dozen rather broken-down-looking hansoms at the entrance to the Park. I jumped into one and told the driver to go to Madison Square.[47]

The unfolding and unfolded beauty of *Myrtle* could not have been without the exquisite modulation of styles in its nine parts to show the effects of Myrtle's calm intellectual and spiritual rapture upon nine different witnesses to it.

Seven years before the publication of *The Other Side* Stephen Hudson issued *A True Story*. As he explained in a preliminary note:

> The material of this novel was contained in four volumes which have appeared separately under different titles, and in effect constituted studies for the present complete work.
>
> The author has here reconstructed and reknit the salient elements in their final form.

In these bare words Stephen Hudson accounted for an action that was critical rather than creative. It may have been the result as much of Stephen Hudson's believing that his separately published novels might be lost under the deluge unless he gathered them into one work that could not be overlooked, as of his being dissatisfied with their form.

On the surface it appears that Stephen Hudson obeyed the tropism of his nature that he had confessed at the climax of *Prince Hempseed*: "I always look back rather than forward when I think."[48] As, through his rereading, he re-experienced the past that he had once divided from the parent plant of experience to give it a separate life in his novels, he rejoined his writing to its parent plant, and then subjected it to a new division, a critical one this time, to give the world a hardier and more sustained artistic experience.

The change one notices first in *A True Story* (1930) is that the novels selected for the volume were rearranged so that a reader could now follow the natural time-order of Richard Kurt's life, instead of the order of creative release. *Prince Hempseed*, written third, opens *A True Story. Elinor Colhouse,* the second to be written, is next, and *Richard Kurt* is third. The "Postscript" is the ninth memoir taken from *Myrtle*. *Tony, Richard, Myrtle and I,* and eight-ninths of *Myrtle* were excluded. *The Other Side* had not yet been written, of course, in 1930.

Prince Hempseed and *Elinor Colhouse* passed through the critical advisement unchanged. They were studies whose intentions had been perfectly fulfilled.

Richard Kurt was trimmed down. Superfluous explanations were cut out; character sketches that stood out from a descriptive scene and were not essential to it, or that struck a satirical and distracting tone, were removed. A block of four chapters, the second to the fifth, was dropped, with its account of Richard's experiences in Brussels, Biarritz, and Paris, to impel the story more directly toward the climax at Como. The episode of Elinor's abortion was removed from Chapter VIII, when Violet Schiff persuaded her husband that Richard's judging Elinor for that act made him out to be the moral prig he had ceased being. Meanings were clarified. One example of such a change occurs in a paragraph at the end of Chapter XI, section ii, describing a thought of Richard's after a sexual bout with Virginia. In *Richard Kurt* it had been phrased, "How had he come to throw off the spell?" The new reading is, "Was it inevitable that repulsion should succeed attraction, that physical gratification should entail moral disgust?" Nothing strictly essential to the design was removed from *Richard Kurt*.

The omission of *Richard, Myrtle and I* kept all reference to Richard's becoming a novelist apart from the story of Richard the person. The exclusion of *Tony* and of eight of the nine memoirs comprising *Myrtle* produces the unity of a concentration upon Richard Kurt, but also halts the forward direction of Stephen Hudson's creativity by restoring the ascendancy of the painful past.

In 1937 Stephen Hudson filled in the last gap remaining in that past with *The Other Side,* and then went on cutting down *Richard Kurt,* removing what he felt to be dispensable, rephrasing passages for clarity. In its final form it contains no reference to Mary Mackintyre.

The last version of *A True Story* appeared in 1948, four years after Stephen Hudson's death. It includes *Prince Hempseed, The Other Side,* and *Elinor Colhouse* unchanged; the finally cut *Richard Kurt;* the unchanged ninth part of *Myrtle;* and an Epilogue that Stephen Hudson's widow found among his papers, the perfect tribute in singing prose to the woman whose brain and heart rescued his life and secured his development to classic stature as a novelist.

The present edition of *Richard, Myrtle and I* represents the fulfilment by the surviving member of the triune consortium of the wish Stephen Hudson recorded in a copy of the first edition that he inscribed for John Gawsworth in March, 1932. Then he wrote: "I wish I were going to rewrite this book; instead I must write my name in it because you want me to. . . ."[49]

Violet Schiff's first revision was translated into French by Boudot-Lamotte and published in an abridged form in *La Table Ronde* in April, 1958. At that time she had not yet completed her final revision. The passage of thirty-five years since the original appearance of the book is excellent proof of the vitality of the consortium that was responsible for Stephen Hudson's art. Through his *alter ego, I,* Stephen Hudson had made clear that Violet's part, requiring her closest imaginative sharing in the creative act, was the editing of the mass of manuscript to make the view accord with the vision. *I* wrote: "The consideration and the revision of the earlier material fell to her and it presently became clear that her task involved the difficult operation of adapting such parts as she did not reject to the inchoate scheme which only began taking shape after the fresh work of some weeks had accumulated. Richard was puzzled when she drew his attention to the glaring inconsistencies with which so many closely written pages abounded. . . ."[50] When Richard thought his novel was getting too long, Myrtle said, "Never mind. Write as fully as you like. We can see afterwards what we can take out."[51]

Editing has cleared away inconsistencies in the relationship between *I* and Richard, superfluous explanations, most of the casual characters, acerbities that were reconsidered, overstressed depreciations of Richard's character, and dialogue that overran its subject. Slight rearrangements of narrative order made for smoother progress. The painters, the sculptor, the Anglo-Irish poet and don, the philosopher-poet, the politician, and the super-journalist millionaire were removed. The Jamesian-Europeanized-American and his household remained, because they were too amusing to be discarded, too perfect in their gentle rendering of comedy to be distracting.

The strong antagonism of Richard's family toward his literary ambition; the reference to Proust's race; the contrasts between Proust and Richard, first, with respect to their attitudes toward their age, and second, with respect to the motives that drove their art; and Richard's moment, after he had finished *Richard Kurt,* of questioning his right to go on without being certain of the truth within himself, were taken out.

Richard's chronic nostalgia for maternal softness and the illusions of childhood was cut away, and the reference to periods of neurasthenic exhaustion and resentment over the strain of writing was left out, as commonplace in every writer's existence and no clue to his uniqueness. Richard's dandyism and his pampering by a valet; his bourgeois prejudices and principles; the account of his neo-Christian philosophy; and his reference to the possibility that he might have children were sheared away. *I*'s ridicule of *Concessions* and his satire on the folly of patronizing the genius of a race were cut out.

A vivid scene was introduced to show Richard, weak after an illness and an operation, turning to Myrtle for love and comfort and away from *I* as a loathsome tempter. Another new scene clarifies to Richard the meaning of his affair with Virginia, dramatizing in dialogue what Stephen Hudson had first written as analysis when he introduced it into his 1930 version of *Richard Kurt* as a part of *A True Story*. In this scene Richard complains that *I* had led him to a nauseating experience with Virginia, and *I* enlightens him by explaining that the nausea had produced a curing emesis.

The sparser form strengthens the dramatic impressiveness of Proust's influence upon Richard's spirit. Proust lifted him out of his despair over the blight the war had laid upon England's cultural life, and quickened in him a hopefulness that enabled Richard to resume his spiritual activity as an artist.

Comparing the two versions of *Richard, Myrtle and I* leads one to appreciate the love and the genius for her task with which the master-editor of Stephen Hudson's writing has re-shaped his materials to the exquisitely right effects from center to surface. She has sacrificed many separately worthwhile details to give the utmost unity and dramatic fulfilment to a story that is unique in the history of the English novel. She is as confident as I am that when this tick of time, our age, which favors masses and the massing of society and which dreams of universally imposed values has sickened itself with its intolerance of other diet, common sense will again recognize the discrete element that gives quality to the life of the many. Then Stephen Hudson's art will come into its authority, with its theme of the precarious progress of the pilgrim who would be an artist. He must subdue the chaos of his generic impulses that is his City of Destruction, and be helped by love to reach salvation as an individual.

Stephen Hudson's contemporaries admired him mainly for his character creation. It may well be that a new generation will rediscover him because of his style. A portent of such a rediscovery is Frank O'Connor's nostalgic reference to him in the *New York Times* of January 15, 1961. When he visits secondhand bookstores, he writes, "My eye strays over the shelves, searching for something by the English novelist Stephen Hudson and wondering if his bare, lucid and precise prose was really as good as I once thought it . . ."

The enveloping designation for Stephen Hudson's prose is the one sculptors used to apply to a statue that had no need of any filler of beeswax to cover up flaws in the marble or lapses of the artist's touch: *sin cera*—sincere.[52]

T. E. M. B.

The Knoll
Lansdowne
June, 1961

RICHARD, MYRTLE AND I

At first, my acquaintance with Myrtle was slight and formal. And yet, from the very beginning, a bond was forming itself between her and me, created by my will that my influence on Richard should prevail, a bond that might eventually imply a mutual though unavowable hostility to everything he stood for, to everything he felt or thought or said independently of our triune consortium.

The position in itself as between Richard and me was rendered at once more complex and more interesting by the fact that while I knew all there was to know about him, he knew nothing at all about me. Even before the advent of Myrtle I at times suspected that his contempt for me was tinged with fear; at an embryonic stage of my alliance with her my suspicion was confirmed. He still affected the contempt, but fear was sitting behind the horseman. Now fear, though it begets hate, may have other offspring, of which one is respect, and Richard unconsciously revealed this by adopting or pretending to adopt on occasion my point of view and my ideas. I say pretending to adopt, because he is by nature shy, modest and retiring.

Richard had been married to his first wife Elinor for over twelve years before I caught my first glimpse of her. That glimpse was enough. If his character is an open book to me, Elinor's was a sheet of glass. Only Richard could have got entangled with so obvious, so shallow, so uninteresting a personality, only Richard could have endured the society of an acrid and detestable human clothes-horse for nearly twenty years. Here I reach a point it is necessary to emphasize. Richard is, always has been, in a certain sense, good, that is, a man with a strong sense of right and wrong according to the code of Christian ethics. This implies the possession of what is called conscience, or answerableness to a theological principle of moral behaviour. He stuck to Elinor out of pure Christian goodness and unselfishness. He could have freed himself from her by a word at any time but he never uttered the word because he considered himself accountable for her. I suppose he thought she was the cross he had to bear. He only kicked over the traces when I was there, and then invariably because I made him. I did not do this out of any desire to help him, for his complaisance in his degrading situation so outraged me that I could not have lifted a finger to defend him. It was Elinor herself who provoked my interference and roused me from the passive role of on-looker by some act of indignity that could not be borne in silence. One, and that the final, example will suffice.

I was with them on the Italian lake where Richard had exhausted his fastidious ingenuity and his father's financial patience in constructing and furnishing a villa which was a salient example of the banal and effeminate

luxury, as it was of the tautological taste, of a bourgeois-
ridden period. Here, in a room lined with books and opening onto a terrace looking over the water, it was Richard's
habit to read and write late at night. I had induced him
with great pain and labour to try his hand at expressing
himself in verse. One evening, having drunk copiously at
dinner and elated by what he believed to be the achievement
of a sonnet, he read the lines aloud. She, the woman, tilts
back her head and in an affected drawl: "Do you call that
crazy drivel poetry?" For an instant his rage was too intense for utterance; then, tearing the paper in his hand to
fragments, he threw them in her face. "For such as you,"
he hissed, "the dunghill and the latrine take the place of
Parnassus. Cursed American mosquito!" Richard rushed
from the room. From the dark waters a deep, hoarse voice
called. It was Virginia, Richard's paramour, sailing out the
night.

I wondered what sort of experience I was in for when,
some weeks after his engagement to Myrtle, he sent for me.

"I have sent for you as a matter of urgent necessity. I
do not pretend that what I have to say, what I have decided
on, will be agreeable to you. I have made up my mind
finally to part with you. Your influence is more than destructive, it is a virulent and deadly poison. You have always
been my evil genius."

For the first time there was a positive note in his voice,
there was resolve in his gesture. His spirit was the organism
upon which my life-giving bacillus must feed to develop
and procreate itself unceasingly. That much I knew. It was

a secret knowledge which I had slowly and painfully acquired, a knowledge hidden from him, hidden from all
who had ever known him, from all but one who ever would
know him. That one was Myrtle. She did not yet know,
but this daughter of Pharaoh had, by a strange and inex-
plicable wisdom, intuitive and occult, discovered the basket
in the bulrushes. These thoughts flashed nakedly through
my mind in all their clear integrity. I knew the law, I was
its prophet. How could I quail before my servant?

"Very well, Richard, it shall be as you will—on one
condition."

He lifted his head contemptuously.

"It is for me to make conditions, for you to accept them."

"At least you can hear what I have to say."

"Say on."

"If Myrtle approves of your decision, I accept it."

"Can you imagine—do you for an instant flatter yourself
that she, who loves me, would desire the continuance of
an association which would embitter our happiness?"

"You use words in a sense I don't understand. What
do you mean by happiness?"

"The antithesis of everything you represent. You have
been directly associated with some of the most miserable
moments of my life."

"Such as?"

"My nauseous experience with Virginia."

"Nauseous? Was I responsible for the emetic? It was
through my revelation of her obliquity that you finally threw
her over."

"I refuse to go into the past. I will talk to Myrtle."

The hour had come when I must fight. Nothing less than my self-preservation was at stake. There was no doubt in my mind that, unless Myrtle intervened, Richard would now finally get rid of me. He was, after all, to that extent I had underestimated him, resolved to reconstruct his life, and he had evidently succeeded in convincing himself that, as long as I was in any way mixed up with him, the reconstruction he had in mind would be impossible. This was, in fact, serious. Moreover, I could not, at that time, feel any confidence in Myrtle's venturing openly to espouse my cause. She had but discovered the infant, and its life would remain a fragile affair until she had provided it with a robust wet-nurse or at least a nourishing food-extract. I determined to speak to her alone. I had never done so hitherto and it was no easy matter, for she was watched and guarded night and day by social experts as vigilant as any of Pharaoh's janissaries.

At this turning-point, luck once more came my way. After I left Richard he was seized with excruciating pain and an immediate operation was decided upon.

Myrtle took matters in hand and obtained the services of the best surgeon and at her order nurses arrived, a special mattress, special pillows.

The operation was duly performed.

Richard is recovering from the anaesthetic, Myrtle sits beside the bed, her eyes fixed on his pallid countenance. He is rambling confusedly. She bends her head close to the pillow to catch his murmurs.

"It's the same . . . It's all part of the same . . . the same thing . . . I see now . . . I see . . ."

His eyes open slowly and take in Myrtle—she puts her hand on his. "I understand now," he says feebly. "Wonderful! Wonderful!"

"Understand what?" she asks.

He turns his head slowly away from her and an expression of supreme disgust spreads over his features, his eyes close. There is silence. The nurse moves forward, and whispers:

"You'd better leave now, he's asleep."

He opens his eyes again.

"No I'm not. Don't leave me, Myrtle."

He lifts her hand to his lips feebly—then suddenly seems to realise my presence and says:

"Go away. I hate you."

The instant the words reached me I felt as though a spell had been broken and I was free again. Myrtle looked grave.

Everything now turned on Myrtle's attitude. She was a woman who never acted upon impulse, or, it would be truer to say, whose impulses were the result of a fusion of intuition and conscious intelligence. Yet I doubted whether she herself knew why she needed my presence at the bedside. It struck me that I might have to divine and turn to my own use those intuitional resources of which she was hardly conscious. Richard's intelligence only enabled him to explore one hemisphere of Myrtle's personality. He could roam as he pleased over that. But there was another which contained great seas and continents, tropical forests and arctic zones undreamt of by him, sensed by me, in whose depths and vastnesses strange sights might be seen, unheard-of creatures might be encountered, and memorable emotions might be experienced. It was now my task to win the freedom and gain the resources I needed to explore this new world.

The scene of our next meeting was Venice, for which Richard's intermittent nostalgia hankered. Myrtle, who had heard just enough about Venice to be sure she would exceedingly dislike it, had prevailed upon Richard to avoid the town and stay at the Lido. Here I found them in a large, empty modern hotel facing the sandy beach on which, in spite of Richard's taste for mildewed and musty relics of the past, they had been spending the greater part of every day, frequenting the city only in the evenings, and then, as far as Myrtle could contrive, limiting their peregrinations to the Piazza and the Grand Canal. As to this, Richard had been nursing a grievance which he introduced very soon after my arrival.

"Here we've been in Venice for over a week, and we haven't seen the inside of a single church. It was as much as I could do to persuade Myrtle to spend half an hour in the Doges' Palace . . ."

"Why should she? Why should anyone if they don't want to?" I asked.

"Because it's part of a civilized being's education."

"There are different forms of education. Myrtle doesn't

like your kind. What have Paolo Veronese, Titian and Bellini got to do with modern civilization?"

Richard flared up. "I wasn't alluding to aeroplanes and motor-cars. I meant culture."

"You meant the opposite of what you said. We'll let that pass. But Myrtle isn't interested in your alleged culture. She has no use for the storied past."

"Are you arguing that we have nothing to learn from the past, that we're to sweep it away?"

"Certainly not. But those who gaze backwards sooner or later become passive onlookers at life, whereas those who gaze forward like Myrtle are active or potentially active agents."

"I don't believe in such generalizations. One can be compounded of both."

"No. They're mutually destructive forces. Whatever survives of the past must survive by reason of its vitality. It has no right to be preserved at the expense of the present. For Myrtle with her strong love of life Venice is an un-wholesome and malodorous mummy, a cankerous conglom-eration of sewers and slums where pseudo-cultured and sentimental aesthetes poke about and stare at the deliques-cent ruins of an old culture that has nothing in common with the modern world."

"And you want her to be one of the rabble that hates everything beautiful?"

"If the rabble thought as she does, it would be healthier. The rabble that can get about revels in absurd anachro-nisms like the gondola, glories in serenading minstrels, hugs itself with delight in sentimental banality."

"You deny that Venice inspires?"

"I deny that a modern artist can get a stimulus from Venice. No fine mind has found itself in Venice since Goldoni. Byron, Musset, Ruskin were bemused by the Venetian miasmas, Wagner was killed by them."

The only point of the discussion was that it enabled me to express what I knew to be in the mind of Myrtle, but it wasn't until the evening that I got my chance of achieving the object for which she had summoned me.

They were sitting at a table outside Richard's favourite coffee tavern, a place frequented by small functionaries and dilettantes of the brush. Hard by stood a fruit stall, a red, green and yellow mass, from which the hot May sun had distilled a sickly and putrescent odour. Richard was expatiating on the lovely architecture of the Campo while Myrtle, scenting the decaying fruit, cast uneasy eyes at the group sitting, heads together, round the neighboring table, talking in excited but subdued tones. Suddenly she started.

"They're talking of cholera," she whispered. "Listen!"

They were silent, trying to catch such words as the unfamiliar Venetian dialect allowed them to seize.

"Five cases today." "Four deaths." "No? Si! Si, davero!" They gesticulated mutely with head-shakings.

"You heard that?" Myrtle whispered to her husband. Her eyes were clouded with apprehension.

Richard blew smoke from his nose.

"Pooh! There are always cases of cholera here in summer. Ships from the Far East, the Levant."

"Horrible. Let's get away—at once."

"Myrtle darling! Run away because some fools at a café . . ."

I broke in.

"Functionary fools. Maritime-customs fools, quarantine fools."

"We're safe enough at the Lido."

Obstinate simpleton.

"If your own body is nothing to you, consider Myrtle's. To the British Consul now. He'll confirm."

A short search ran him to earth. In confidence, cholera was rampant. Figures difficult to get, of course, Venice depended on tourists, the season would be killed. Better get out.

They took the train for Switzerland at midnight.

Richard and Myrtle had returned from their honeymoon and had gone to a south-coast resort to join her aged father, who was taking his annual summer change. I had not seen them since Venice.

"I'm going to tell you something curious, something I should never have believed possible. It's something to do with Myrtle, at least so it seems to me."

Richard was almost genial towards me.

"Yes," he went on, "it seems more curious than ever, in these surroundings."

The surroundings were a large old-fashioned smoking-room at the back of the hotel-building where we were in the habit of sitting in the evening, to get away from the crowd. We were in the corner by a writing-table, between the large open fireplace and a window. In deep leather armchairs, two elderly retired judges or colonels were slumbering peacefully. The time was almost ten at night. The month was August. He drew his seat close to the writing-table, took up a pen, dipped it in the ink, and began writing.

Two hours passed.

Richard was sitting by a bed on which Myrtle lay. A lamp on a table by her side threw its light upon her upturned face and upon the sheets of paper from which he was reading aloud.

At his heart lay an indescribable oppression. This gulf between him and the past was unbridged by the hurried sequence of those necessary acts which had filled the intervening days. The happening of every hour filled his memory . . .

The phrases followed each other in a cool even stream. "Do you think it's any good?" He was addressing Myrtle.

"Yes, I think so. What made you suddenly start on that?"

"I don't know exactly. I was trying to explain, to— Wait a minute."

He put the sheets down on her bed, her leg was under them, and they fluttered to the floor. He clasped his hands across his forehead, unclasped them, stared at her.

"It's never happened to me before. I felt I had to write, and he—and he—" he turned his eyes away from her slowly, "he made me do it, he put the words into my head." He looked bewilderedly at her. "It's very curious, isn't it?"

Myrtle lay back, regarding her husband thoughtfully.

"Would you go on with it?'" he asked her.

"Certainly I would, if you and he—" she paused. "If you and he agree to work together."

"It's nothing to do with me. I don't know what he's writing about. I'm not in the least interested in all that. It may be worth doing, I can't say. It isn't the way I see things, not in the least."

Richard stared, his expression of incredulity bore the stamp of honesty.

"But you made me do it."

"You knew what you were writing, didn't you?"

"Of course I knew. If I hadn't known, I couldn't have written sense. Whatever it is, the stuff's sane enough."

He took up the sheets from the floor and began reading them to himself.

"Yes, it's sane," I said, "but it doesn't seem to me to matter—all that about your mother's death and what you were feeling."

"It may not matter to you. It matters to me. Besides, damn it—" he stuffed the sheets into his pocket, "it must matter to you or you wouldn't have made me do it."

"Unconscious application of energy. It's a pity you have the use of it. However, that can't be helped at present.'"

Again Richard is sitting at the same table. He is reading over what he has written and punctuates his silent reading with little expressions such as: "That's all right. I must put in something there," and so on.

"Have a look at it," he says.

And let me tell you that's the only way ever to get a foot-hold in English society of the right kind. I know about these

things—I understand society. I never much cared myself, but
I care for your sake . . .

"I can't make head or tail of it, it seems to me meaning-
less."

"That's because it doesn't follow on from what I was
reading last night. This is another part."

"Nothing to do with that. I understand the meaning of
the words well enough. I can't see the use of writing them.
There's no point in it. Who cares about such rubbish?"

"Elinor cared. Can't you understand that I'm expressing
something I've been through, something that I've suffered
from?"

"Suffered from! What did you put up with it for? I tried
hard enough to get you away. But what's the good of going
back to it? Leave the past in peace."

"I can't. I can't reconstruct the present till I've settled up
the past."

Had I got to lend myself to this?

"How long will that take you?" I asked.

"How am I to know? It depends on you—not me."

He depended on me to get hold of his past and I depended on him for my present existence. What had I in
common with the people he was writing about, with the
lives they lived, with their thoughts, their ambitions, their
pains? What did the physical life and material or immaterial
satisfaction of these ghosts of a dead past matter to me?
This force, wherever it came from, whatever its purpose,
seemed to be perverse and ruthless once it asserted itself.
Its ruthlessness I had no objection to. That could be turned

to advantage. But the perversity. There must be some means of dealing with that.

"Let me think it over," I said.

Richard gathered up the sheets and, head cast down, went slowly to the door.

Work, if this singular use of time could be so called, continued under the same conditions for many evenings. As Richard's enthusiasm grew, the hours of our curious collaboration extended until they encroached further and further upon the night. After a prolonged sitting, some weeks later, we went upstairs. Myrtle was lying awake, reading, and looked up from her book as we entered. Her face expressed a certain uneasiness but she made no remark, waiting for Richard to start reading aloud as usual.

"I don't think I'll read it to you tonight," he said, "you must be tired and it's late."

"Oh. Never mind, do."

"Besides, I'm not pleased with what I've done. Up till now it has gone all right but this evening I've got a feeling that I've gone wrong. I don't seem to have written what I wanted to write."

"Well, let me hear."

He didn't answer but fumbled with the sheets, reading a few lines here and there.

"It's got nothing to do with—with—"

"With what, darling?"

"You see, I want to deal with the past. I want to straighten it out—"

"Well?"

"This isn't about the past. It's all jumbled up. It's what's in my mind in a way but it isn't—it isn't ripe."

"Read it anyhow. Perhaps I shan't agree with you."

"All right, I will. But I know it's no good."

He held the sheets under the lamp and read.

Myrtle at the time when Richard Kurt entered her life was a creature at once unusually mature and yet unformed. Mature in character and in an unconscious wisdom of her own which her intelligence served without effort; an unselfish intelligence, demanding no autonomy and limited to daily exercise, moderate in measure and restricted in scope. She had always taken the easiest path, less because it was easy than because her wisdom recommended it. Life had so far demanded of her no special enterprise; her always serene spirit prevailed over impatience of obstacles to a freer development of mind and accepted a passive attitude towards Life. Perhaps because it had never been called upon to resist shock, this spirit was not only equal to the assault of events for which it had had no preparation but reintegrated itself in a wholly new attitude, as active and determined as it had hitherto been passive and indifferent. Though at first the impact of a personality, so antithetic to the continuity and sobriety of the Vendramin tradition, was masked by convention, Myrtle was not for an instant deceived. She fully realized and as fully accepted the implications of her sponsorship. Outward appearance, manners and behavior never concealed from her that "Kurt" was of a type unfamiliar to any member of her family. She knew from the start that she was going to have her hands full and that the technique of dealing with a character of this kind would have to be learnt as she went along. At the beginning these considerations occupied her hardly at all. Thought was playing second fiddle to sentiment. Was he really coming into her life? was a much more urgent question

than what she would do with him when he got there. For
though he had asked her to marry him the same day as he had
left his wife and she had immediately accepted him, a year
must pass before he could be free and they were at the first
days of it. She had no certainty of the rightness of her intuition about him, an intuition which, however unlimited its
potentiality, as yet only informed her that whatever he was,
he was not what he believed himself to be. What others
thought about him, his familiars if any or his family, mattered
to her only in so far as their opinions might affect or influence him. Her intuition first, its confirmation by her reason
afterwards, these were the only arbitrators. There was no lying in wait, no conscious scrutiny, hardly observation. The
day-to-day, the hour-to-hour Richard would, she knew, reveal
himself in his being and becoming as present glided into
future, as future became present, then past, then history.

While he read, Myrtle sat up in the bed, leaning on
her elbow, listening with dilating eyes. When he reached
the last words she stared at Richard without speaking.

"You see. It's not what I meant to write at all. It's like
someone else writing about us as we were a short time ago.
I shall have to tear it up and begin again."

"No. No. Don't do that." Myrtle was still staring at
him, then suddenly she became aware of me. The head of
the bed and Myrtle's night-clad figure were in the half-
light of the lamp which shed all its light towards Richard
but downwards on the papers in his hand.

"He certainly must have made you write that."

"You think so?" I said. "Well, you see, I'm investigating
and I thought I'd try a little experiment, and I can't discover what the force is without experiment. You're con-

cerned with writing this book. You said you couldn't do it
without me, that you'd written what I made you write. I
told you, I didn't want you to write anything, that what you
read had no meaning for me. Are we agreed so far?"

"Yes."

"I told you I should have to think it out. It's a very difficult business. I'm only at the beginning of it. But I think
I've discovered something—"

Neither of them spoke.

"I think now that you've read that—I see my way to—"

I stopped because I realised I was just going to give myself away. I had been going to say: "I think I see my way to
liberating myself." That wouldn't suit Richard. He wanted
to write his book. The force was only of importance to him
in so far as it enabled him to do that. I must use my craft.

"I'll put it another way," I said lightly. "I think Myrtle
comes in here."

I knew I couldn't manage him without her.

"I'll do anything I can to help you—anything," she said.

Richard interrupted petulantly.

"To help him. Why him? It is I who need your help.
What does it matter about him?"

Myrtle put out her hand and stroked his hair.

"It matters for your own sake. If I help him, that is, if I
can help him, he'll help you. Won't you?" she asked.

"I don't know," I answered. "I don't want to help anyone,
but if he wants to write that book, apparently he can't do
it without me. I've no objection to his trying. I don't care
whether he writes it or not. I only care about the force and
how it can be used."

"What do you want me to do?" she asked.

"It isn't so much what I want you to do as what you want yourself. If you want to help me, you can help me. I think I can say I know that."

"How shall I begin?"

I couldn't tell her that the only way she could help me was by suppressing Richard, by using all her influence on my side. She was in love with Richard, not with me. As yet she only wanted to help me because Richard needed me. The only prudent course for me was to appear to subordinate myself to Richard's purpose, which, for the moment, was writing this, to me, completely futile book. The reading of this evening had confirmed the value of my experimental investigations. I should use that knowledge in my own way, subtly and gradually. I answered her question by another.

"Do you want Richard to write?"

She cast a gently inquiring glance at her husband and answered slowly, doubtfully: "I don't know."

"I don't either," he responded; "perhaps it's a disease, but after I've done a few pages I feel a sort of relief."

"It's a fearfully boring undertaking," I said. "Couldn't you drop all that early part and get down to the present?"

"Go on from where I read this evening you mean?" I felt him wavering under me.

"Possibly. Treat the past as summarily as possible and retrospectively."

He fidgeted nervously, trying to extricate himself from my toils.

"What objection have you to the past? One must live

in the past, part of the time, whether one likes it or not."

Myrtle asserted her opinion resolutely. "I don't."

"No. You're exceptional. Besides, you're satisfied with your past—I'm not."

"All the more reason to turn your back on it," I said.

"I will when I've laid it to rest," Richard answered gloomily.

"I'll help you give it its quietus if you'll make a bargain with me."

"What is the bargain?"

"I'll submit to the exactions of your past if you'll stand the cost of my future."

"How can I when I don't know what is involved?"

"I don't know what horse's work I shall be in for, laying your ghosts," I said. "The effort may use up all my energy. You've got the best of the bargain. We live today. To-morrow—? But I'm ready to chance it."

Here again my reserves of knowledge came to my aid. I knew, as he did not, that however wearisome the task of this writing might be, I should be enabled by the continuous co-operation to pursue my investigations into the significance and uses of the mysterious force that made that co-operation possible. I knew further that during the reconstruction of his uninteresting and wasted past, I should be laying the foundations for a future which I should dominate. Moreover, confident as ever in my powers, I believed that this was the inevitable course prescribed by destiny for my fulfilment.

The bargain was not struck. If it had been, Richard, whatever his intention, would have failed to act up to it.

Consistency of purpose was foreign to his temperament. He was incapable of sustained perseverance even in what he himself wanted to do.

The next day he made an attempt to resume his writing, changing the hour to late afternoon. The attempt was abortive. We were in the same room at the back of the hotel, the quietude of which was not even troubled by the post-prandial snorers. He sat down at the usual table, took the usual pen in his hand. Some minutes passed. Then, throwing down his pen, he exclaimed:

"I can't work when I've got something else in my mind. My uncle wants us to join him in Hamburg. My two old aunts are keen on seeing Myrtle. I can't very well refuse, and I want to go abroad anyhow."

"The bargain's off then, is it?"

"Not off. Postponed. I can't work while I'm away, so it's no use going on now."

"Quite so. You don't need me, that's certain. It doesn't matter in the least, only next time you may find you'll have to pay a bigger price for my co-operation. I don't change my mind so easily as you do."

I am in a large square room that seems in a manner familiar to me. With their backs to me, Richard, Myrtle and three other figures are gazing at two pictures, masterly and vital portraits of a middle-aged man and a middle-aged woman, amazingly strong and resilient personalities, dressed in the fashion of the end of the eighteenth century. Of the three figures, one, a man of short square build, is muttering. He doesn't turn. He is absorbed in the portraits.

"Thou Nathaniel! Thou Johanna! Look down upon us.

Theophilus, William, married among strangers. Now they are gone. Both begat sons but the old stock is dying out, dying out. They cannot make, they cannot hold.

"Richard, weaker son of a weak father, has no issue; Anthony, a wastrel, what can his boy become? Theo's two boys are not of us. Their Mother's God is not our God, her people are not our people. We are dying out."

It was Frederick Kurt who turned and, without speaking, looking downwards, walked slowly across the room. I caught his grim, firm profile, the thin shaven lips, the "trifle of whisker," the air of "self-confidence and self-esteem," and, over all, the shadow of the past, the shadow of death. One by one, the others followed him, except Myrtle, who sat down at an open grand piano and, playing a few chords, sang in a low voice:

> Die arme Seele spricht zum Leibe:
> Ich lass' nicht ab von dir, ich bleibe
> Bei dir—ich will mit dir versinken,
> In Tod und Nacht, Vernichtung trinken!

Her eyes wandered from the keys to the portraits.

> O, Das ist grauenhaft; O bleib,
> Bleib bei mir, du geliebter Leib!

She rose from the piano and, as we approached the half-open folding doors, a lady, hidden behind one side of them, came forward, put her arms about her and kissed her.

An Italianate room with the inevitable ornate bookshelves, masses and masses of books; Richard pulls one out and looks at it; a bronze bust here, Dante, another there, Voltaire, an oil painting of a *Madonna con bambini*, carved arm-chairs, red damask coverings, large writing-table with massive bronze inkstand, at which sits a tired-looking man of fifty, white-haired, high-browed, Jamesian-Europeanized-American, whose eyes follow Richard examining his books, through the window to a terrace, beyond the terrace a slope with parterres beflowered, beyond that a lake. This was another of Richard's "old friends", living that exemplary and regulated life of dignified and cultured somnolence that so much appealed to him. How these people love lakes, how they accumulate books! Myrtle talking to a woman beside her on a red damask sofa, a woman of less than forty, a pretty-pretty, worried, nervous, dark-eyed face, talking about the woman's disease or whatever it is, a form of neurasthenia apparently; Myrtle is being solicitous.

"I call them spasms, they come on quite unawares. But I'm much better than I was. Boiton is a genius. He has a marvellous system, entirely his own invention. He's written a book about it."

Myrtle, playing sympathetic eyes upon the invalid: "What is the system?"

"It's through the mind, you must control your body through your mind. Everything has to pass through the mind. D'you see what I mean? I mean, d'you see what he means?"

Myrtle nods.

"I have to do exercises, mental discipline exercises he calls them. When I wake at night I have to repeat certain sentences like 'I'm lying in bed. There's nothing the matter

with me. Presently I shall go to sleep again.' That calms
me and prevents the spasm coming and I generally do go
to sleep."

Myrtle nods again but her eyes seek escape. A dark-
haired girlish-looking youth enters the room and stands
behind the sofa. The tired face of the man at the writing-
table brightens, his eyes gleam.

"Adolph knows all about it, don't you, Adolph?"

The boy, he is little more, smiles at Myrtle, and answers
in French. "Yes, yes, dear, but you mustn't talk about it, it's
bad for you."

"But she asked me, didn't you Mrs. Kurt, Myrtle I
mean? You did, didn't you?"

Richard joins the group.

"Do you remember our trips in the mountains, Mr. Kurt,
Richard, I mean? Wasn't it lovely?"

Myrtle extricates herself.

"The woman's daft," I whispered; "why doesn't he lock
her up?"

"He wouldn't think he had the right to his compensation
unless he paid the price," Myrtle answered.

The tall, thin Jamesian figure rises from the writing-
table and comes to the sofa.

"Time for you to lie down before you do your exercises,
Maisie dear."

Maisie gets up at once obediently and, smiling all round,
goes out of the room. The white-haired man lays his arm
on the shoulder of the boy, looking down on him with a
world of love in his eyes.

"Shall we take them for a stroll, Adolph?"

The boy smiles back at him.

I took counsel with myself. I began to consider and meditate upon the inner meaning and power of love. What was love? I had no erudition. My ignorance weighed heavily on me. It was not the least of the long list of penalties I was called upon to pay through my early dependence on Richard. And yet, perhaps, in some respects I was not so much the loser as I seemed. Had I been steeped in the lore of the past, some part of my own speculative energies would almost certainly have been exhausted. What, for instance, had the limited and eclectic collection of poets, philosophers and scholars whose works, in spite of his idle existence, Richard had gathered and to which, in consequence, I had access, taught me about love? That love is a passion, an illusion, a disease, a poison, that it transforms, inspires, illuminates, destroys; that it lifts up, that it casts down, that it is selfish, that it is unselfish, that it is moral, that it is physical, that it is eternal, that it is momentary, that it makes the strong weak and the weak strong, that it makes brave men cowards and cowards brave men, that it makes men stupid and women intelligent, that it makes the young old and the old young, that it frees men and makes them slaves, that youth despises it and runs after it, that age sneers at it and longs for it. In short, that love's forms are as varied as life itself, that it is of the essence of life itself. This was all very well, but what did it really amount to, what conclusion had the researches of all these sages really led to? It seemed to me just exactly nothing, though each one appeared to think he had contributed an unique and priceless discovery to the wisdom of mankind.

No. The contemplation of love in this general fashion would only add my insignificant quota to the universal ignorance. It behooved me to consider not what love was but the nature of Myrtle's particular love. Again I saw the rightness of an earlier conclusion. Myrtle, unlike other women, was not satisfied with loving and being loved. She meant to use her love. Where I had gone wrong was in assuming that in whatever way she used it, I stood to gain. I was more dangerously wrong in telling myself that it was immaterial whether she kept the reins in her own hand or abandoned them to me. Hereafter my main purpose must be to wrest them from her hand. The issue was becoming clear. It was no longer a struggle between Richard and me for domination. It was Myrtle's love for Richard against my life-force, against the power itself which operated through me. What should now be my line of action? I must at all costs preserve my intellectual autonomy. If I didn't look out, Myrtle would seize upon my thought-stuff and use it to nourish Richard's brain, like a mothering bird which pecks a mass of food into fragments tiny enough for its chick's digestive and assimilative capacity.

Richard was coming closer to me. His curiosity about types with which he was unfamiliar was an indication of mental activity. This must be encouraged. Boredom with his environment was the necessary preliminary to eventual rupture with the hidebound obstructionists whose influence until now had prevailed against mine.

The next time I was summoned a surprise was in store for me.

"I've asked you to come to tell you I've given it all up," Richard said.

"Given what up?'" I asked.

"The whole business. I'm sick of everything—"

Myrtle appeared as smiling and gay as usual.

"Not of love, I hope?"

"I'm serious," he replied. "I'm sick of all the people I meet. They understand nothing about life, and their self-complacence is unbearable. We've decided to go away. I'm going to work."

This was indeed unexpected.

"What at?" I asked.

"I'm going to write." There was a challenge in his expression.

"What about?"

"I've got a novel in my mind. I can't talk about it but it's there. She'll help me think it out."

I could read in Myrtle's face no endorsement of the sanguine expectation.

He continued: "It won't be anything like the one I began before, you know. That was your doing, not mine. My own ideas are quite different."

"I'm delighted to hear it. But I must remind you that I entirely disowned any collaboration in the first instalment and I was only trying an experiment in the second."

"This time I'm going to get away from myself altogether. I've done with myself, I'm going to lose myself in others."

"I congratulate you on getting rid of a troublesome obsession. It's a step forward to put the past behind you. Go ahead."

If Richard carried out his intention, what, I asked myself, was he going to put into his novel? In itself, whether he wrote one or not was of no importance, but his announcement was an indication of his state of mind and, if accomplished, the performance might be valuable to me as a chart of his psychological explorations. There was no chance of my asserting my supremacy until he discovered for himself the limits of his unaided powers. The stage in his development now reached was that of an embryonic reassessment of values under an influence of which he was unaware and of which, so far as I could judge, Myrtle too was only in a measure conscious. He supposed, doubtless, that his preliminary seeking-out of individuals he could here and there distinguish as representing activities that were known to him theoretically as intellectual and artistic, was a spontaneous effort to reconstruct his life intelligently. It was, of course, nothing of the sort. He was simply turning away from his inherited and acquired environment as a result of my exposure of its futility, a futility which I purposely emphasized on purely selfish grounds to the point of excluding pleasant and natural human relationships. It was a necessary part of my strategy to deprive him of every resource I could not control. A nature as sensitive, as plastic as Richard's yielded so readily to every sentimental attraction and moral influence that if I did not succeed in making him keep his and Myrtle's kith and kin, and their concerns, at a distance, he might easily become one of them. And here Myrtle was not altogether to be counted on. She was well-disposed towards me, she had given me more encouragement than I had dared hope for, but she was painfully amenable to familial affection and obligation. Added to this, her nature was an extraordinarily fertile territory through which confluents and tributaries of love and sympathy flowed naturally and without the slightest obstacle into the main-stream of her life. These waters were open free gratis to all who cared to use them, and it stands to reason that they weren't going to give them up without a struggle. Their departure seemed, therefore, to be a move in my favour and I congratulated myself that the only influence on Richard would be Myrtle's.

Richard and Myrtle returned and the novel was published. During that period I never saw them. Before it was in print he sent for me.

"You were right, the novel is rotten. But I'm not beaten. I see where I went wrong. I'm going to write another."

I was silent.

"This time I'm going to draw upon real experience but I'm going to invent a setting. There's something sordid about one's own reality. I'm going to find another one. What's the good of experience if I don't use it?"

"I don't know."

My answer seemed to puzzle him.

"It must be good for something," he said, after a pause.

"It's good for oneself if it doesn't cost too much," I said. "One pays all sorts of prices for it. But men have to realise experience in terms they can identify and relate."

"In my case that means reliving pain, and no one wants to dwell on trouble when it's over."

"Is that why you don't want to write about yourself?" I asked.

"I do and I don't. It's very odd but when you're there—" he looked at Myrtle and repeated, "when he's there, I do— at least, I feel I must."

"I'm rather a depressing companion, in fact."

"Not exactly." Again his eyes appealed to Myrtle. "It's as though writing about myself were the only way to get rid of myself. What would you do?" He addressed Myrtle.

"What do you think?" she asked me.

"If you remember," I answered, "I offered long ago to submit to the exactions of your past if you would stand the cost of my future. You neither accepted nor declined my offer. I hold to it."

"I'm not ready to decide yet. If I can't get rid of myself without, I suppose I shall have to."

Nothing happened. He never began that book.

When the war burst upon us, my intercourse with Richard and Myrtle became fragmentary. I caught occasional glimpses of them, popping out as I had once planned in wholly different circumstances and with a very different object in view, but my appearances were surreptitious. Self-interest if not self-preservation made it necessary for me to keep not only out of Richard's way but out of the way of men. I never was adept at concealing my opinions whether about men or about things, and had I come into the open during a time when King Fool reigned, any jack-

anapes might have caused me to be laid by the heels. My
brief emergences are not noteworthy. The most my occasional appearances could accomplish under war conditions
was to remind Richard that there was another point of view
besides the universally current one and to reinforce his
failing belief in the final vindication of intelligence as the
motive agent of human conduct. There was actually no
field of operation for the mind while the world was running
mad. These years contained days which were not without
profit to me, in spite of enforced inactivity. I had always
known that the growth of the human mind was a slow
business measured in terms of an individual experience, and
the war, if it had no other effect on my own, taught it the
value of patience. The effects of the war had made themselves felt in the entourage of my associates, who were
mainly occupied with the concerns of the unhappy young
generation which was called upon to pay flesh-and-blood
tribute to omnipotent Folly. The removal at an early stage
of Myrtle's father had lifted a load from her heart. He, at
least, was spared the bitterest experience. Others, both close
and distant, all less ripe, followed him at intervals into
silence, swallowed up in the cloud of poisonous vapour that
hung over the distracted world. Many social landmarks
had been or were being swept away and the whole structure
of society was threatened with dissolution. The hurricane
of death had blown down the main buttresses of the old
order and whistled through the unsuspected crannies and
crevices their destruction had revealed. In the last year I
was sent for. Almost all that could happen had happened,

and faintly, like a very minute and barely distinguishable star, Reason began to glimmer.

Richard and Myrtle had taken a house in a distant part of the country where, at his wit's end to know what to do, he had engaged in agricultural enterprise on a small scale. I found him in a somewhat depressed state, his crops, whatever they were, were promising badly and his cows or pigs were suffering from a mysterious malady that puzzled the wits of the ex-huntsman, an acquaintance of former days, with whom he had formed a sort of temporary farming partnership. Myrtle approached me:

"I want your help. I can't let Richard go on like this. He hasn't opened a book for months. I can't even get him to read Proust."

"Who is Proust?" I asked.

"Proust is my newest and best friend, the only friend the war has brought me."

"What does he think about it?"

"He doesn't say. He deals with an earlier period."

"That may be important now that there is an earlier period."

Richard dressed in breeches and leggings, with a hunting-crop in his hand, threw himself wearily into a chair.

"That bloody mare pulls my arms out of their sockets.'"

"Good God! Have you started that sort of thing again?" I asked.

"One must get about. We gave up our car long ago. Horses are the only things I know anything about. Only

I'm too old for breaking work—" he flung his crop rattling on to the floor, "I'm too old for everything, curse it."

No wonder Myrtle wanted my help.

"What about Proust?" I remarked.

"Proust," he echoed. "Damn Proust. What's the good of Proust with the world in this state? Proust belongs to the past. What we've got to think of is food."

"You can't feed your mind on potatoes," I suggested.

"Have you come here to talk like that? You don't seem to have learnt anything after all we've been through."

"I've come to try and talk sense," I answered. "'Myrtle was telling me Proust is her best friend. I don't know him."

"I'm glad for her sake. He's no good to me."

"How do you know till you read him?" she asked.

"My dear girl, what's the good of asking me that? This isn't a time for reading. Civilization is in ruins and they're at it still."

"Stop a minute," I said, "civilization has never been so active. The whole concern has speeded up. That's not an argument against books, it's an argument in their favour. If you had said it was no use reading before the war, there might have been something in it. But now that civilization is becoming really efficient, some of us can afford to think about Proust and so on."

"I don't see your point. What is this leading to?"

"When the war is over we shall have to begin again," I answered.

"Begin what? The whole thing is broken to pieces. No one will have time for anything except work. There'll be no room for people like me. You don't realise, because you know nothing about that sort of thing. You never read the papers. Reading and writing books is a sheer waste of time."

"It always was, from that point of view," I said.

"No. In the old leisurely world one could do what one pleased. Those who wanted to spend their time hunting or shooting or playing golf could do so. No one minded. The same thing with reading. But all that's changed now. First, the war isn't over. When it is, do you think those millions of men who've been living in hell all these years, will put up with the old state of things? I can tell you they won't."

"I don't know anything about hunting and shooting and golf," I answered. "Can you inform me whether all the packs of hounds have been broken up because what they ate was wanted for the troops, whether the coverts have been destroyed for pit-props and the links ploughed up to grow corn?"

"They may go on still," Richard answered. "But they won't for long."

"Why? If these innocent forms of bourgeois amusement remain in *statu quo ante* after four years of war, there's not much likelihood of peace making an end of them. Don't you believe it. There's nothing your millions would hate more than to come back and find anything changed. The King's on his throne and all's well with England. If that's the strength of your argument against reading Proust, you must show better cause."

"Anyhow, I don't see what I've to gain by reading a long French novel which, as far as I can make out, is about nothing in particular."

"Art never is about anything in particular. Its value is

its complete uselessness. It has nothing to do with modern civilization. It's a thing apart. If it ceased to be that, it would cease to be Art. Apparently such a prospect would not displease you? You're not alone in that."

"I should be neither pleased nor displeased. Art seems to me not to matter in comparison with these other things."

" 'These other things' meaning civilization. I quite agree. It doesn't. But while it exists, it's autonomous in its own realm. It will never interfere with your growing potatoes, if that's the way you want to express yourself."

"I'm not growing potatoes to please myself," Richard stopped.

"Don't deceive yourself. For four years you've been trying to do things you greatly disliked, to conform to the prevailing opinion, and your mind during the same time has gradually become stagnant, your reactions mechanical. Myrtle thinks the moment has come for you to make an effort to get out of this slough."

Richard threw himself back in his seat despondently.

"Myrtle is right, and so are you. I've become a vegetable. But what's to be done? I've ceased to feel I have any right to my own thoughts."

"My prescription for that is to sample those of someone else. The war can't last much longer. Give Proust a chance of seeing you to the end of it."

By Myrtle's urgent wish I remained with them, and for all his objections, Richard began reading Proust. My insistence on this fact is cardinal, for a significant change in his attitude synchronized with his growing absorption in the French novelist who, becoming a staple subject of our talk, provided an invigorating change from the gloom and ennui of war-news. *Du côté de chez Swann* was a chance discovery of Myrtle's; from the first line her enthusiasm was aroused and when she had finished the book it had entered into the fabric of her being. Music and literature had always been worlds into which Myrtle could escape at any suitable season, corresponding for her more nearly to the mystical apartness in which the truly religious live than to spheres of intellectual or artistic interest.

Literature now began to assume a significance in our tripartite relationship, of which at the time we were only partly conscious. The intensity of her interest communicated itself not only to Richard but to me and we found ourselves gluttonously consuming the peculiar form of intellectual nourishment the French hybrid manufactured. The intense individuality of the writer permeated the book to a degree only found in works of the highest order. Once Proust got you, there was no escape from him and his interminable discourse, which was largely about negligible people and the aimless things they said and did. By the mere exercise of his obviously spontaneous verbosity, this epistolary wizard had not only created a new mould for literature, he had imposed upon the French mind a new standard of human values which must inevitably influence European thought and by which, as inevitably, the creative literature of the future must be judged. Here was an end to plot and pretence and subterfuge. Hereafter, for the finer minds, there would be no return of the pseudo-realism of the past. This amazing conversationalist had given a new impetus to psychological research and, by exposing the hollowness of a culture which rested upon social attitudes, had given a new twist to history.

My own mind being thus affected by Proust, I was not altogether surprised when, a little later, Richard announced his intention of going back to his writing. I should in any case have aided and abetted Myrtle in her endeavours to wean him from his pseudo-patriotic preoccupations, for it was to my own interest, but my influence in bringing about this sudden change of mood and inclination was small compared with that of the new and unexpected ally. It stood to reason that my reaction to Richard's announcement now was very different from what it was to his earlier effort. My nature is always prepared for change. Among the stupidities to which the mechanized mind is enslaved, none is more intellectually vitiating than "sticking to one's opinion" when the circumstances that led to a given conclusion have been modified by events. What is true today is as likely as not to be untrue tomorrow, nothing being static in life except dullness. It had never entered my mind that a book could in a fundamental sense alter my outlook, let alone disclose an unsuspected outlet for the force that was driving me onwards. Yet, the reading of Proust had led to this surprising result.

Of what nature was the spell this unknown Frenchman cast over us? Apparently he had spent a lifetime in the observation and accumulation of minute human refractions and had succeeded in controlling and manipulating his infinite loquacity as a means of expelling them in the form of

Art. Therein, surely, was a lesson to profit by. Richard's life, however useless, supplied material which could be used and if he had strength enough to carry me through the swamps and morasses of this past, I might at the end get off his shoulders dryfoot on to the terra firma of the present.

What if, after all, I found it possible to use this apparently inadequate machine for my own purposes? My former experiment was only abortive because Richard, unsupported by my will and by Myrtle's influence, had not the persistence to go on with his enterprise. When, therefore, Richard, rummaging amongst his papers, brought to light a pile of forgotten manuscript and asked me to run my eye over it, I made no demur.

"I feel like tackling this again," he remarked. "But I realise I can't without you. Are you prepared to help me?"

"I've never withdrawn my offer," I answered. "It's still up to you to accept it."

"I've thought it over. I'll take the risk."

While Richard worked, I attempted to determine what my share was in the complex collaboration to which Myrtle was a third party. The consideration and revision of the earlier material fell to her and it presently became clear that her task involved the difficult operation of adapting such parts as she did not reject to the inchoate scheme which only began taking shape after the fresh work of some weeks had accumulated. Richard was puzzled when she drew his attention to the glaring inconsistencies with which many closely written pages abounded.

After much careful scrutiny, Myrtle decided to delete at least three parts of the stuff.

"Don't destroy it. You'll see for yourself when you've finished, if you don't now, that it won't do. What I am discarding is written from a consciousness that would conflict with the rest. It would be like a book written by two different people."

That Richard ended by accepting her decision was of less importance to me than the cause of her criticism. Myrtle's psychological judgments were peculiarly astute. She had not only intuition but a gift, rare among women, of being able to reason. What she said was especially significant for me, because of its bearing upon the obscure connexion between Richard's consciousness and my force. How and when did they intermingle? I could admit no direct responsibility for what he wrote. When he read his day's work aloud to Myrtle, as was his custom, there had so far been little in it that commended itself to me. Most of it seemed to be an exhaustive account of his past life with Elinor, which could have been reduced to a small number of selected episodes. I recognised a certain cumulative value in his method, but my nature is too urgent, too impatient to submit itself to the tedium of a slow detailed report, to which only Proust can, with some difficulty, reconcile me. Knowing, then, that my method of expression would be at the opposite pole to Richard's, I asked myself what part my consciousness could be playing in this business. Some time passed and I had reached no conclusion, when, suddenly one morning he turned to me.

"You remember my affair with Virginia?"

"Yes."

"It's extraordinarily difficult to convey the peculiar effect she had on me. Did you ever grasp what it really was?"

"I've never thought much about it. It was a form of sensuality, of course, and that's a department I've no experience of."

Richard continued: "I had known Virginia some months and seen a good deal of her. You had been absent for some time and suddenly you came into my mind. I remember all the circumstances vividly. It was very hot. I had arranged to meet her by a shrine on the old mule-path above Aquafonti. We climbed up and up together until at a certain point she led me through a wood to a retired spot, a sort of plateau on the shelf of rock which couldn't be overlooked. I threw myself down on the mossy grass. She stood above me, wiping her face, with an amused, teasing expression. 'You're tired, are you?' she said, 'I'm not,' and throwing herself on her knees, she put her arms under my neck and began pulling at me. I took her by the waist and pulled her down and we started a kind of wrestling match, which ended by my throwing and falling on the top of her. She lay on the grass, breathing heavily, exhausted by the struggle, and by that time I was drenched with sweat and too tired to do anything but lie still. She closed her eyes and as I lay there watching her, you again came into my mind. I was afraid. I did not dare to follow my impulse. 'Don't be afraid,' you said. 'Nothing you will do will wake her. You can avail yourself of the situation as much as you please. It's expected of you.' "

"And I was right, wasn't I?"

"You were," Richard answered. "The most intense sensual experience I ever had started from that incident."

I thought a moment and then I said:

"The scene in all its details is fresh in my mind. You have quoted my words quite correctly. What were the circumstances? The girl was a Catholic in the strictly limited sense that peasants are Catholics. She had, in fact, the peasant mentality and found satisfaction in sharing their lives and in adopting their habits and tastes. For her the letter of Church law was everything. All her sins were forgiven and remitted if she confessed—not to you, mind you, that would have been for her the depths of ignominy—but to a priest. So far from that being an unpleasant ordeal, the self-abnegation of the confessional, the humiliation before God in the form of a man, is a definite and well-known form of physical ecstasy, leading in certain cases to hysterical dementia. Thanks to your Library, I've read Havelock Ellis and Freud. My words to you were suggested by a typical example of female lust."

Richard was silent a moment, evidently thinking over my words.

"And yet I should never have known that she was feigning sleep in order to tempt me to possess her if you hadn't put it into my head. I no longer feel hostile to you—on the contrary, I want to live on good terms with you—but I can't deny to myself that your influence upon me then was an evil one. You made me realise that her very guile was what fascinated me because her desire was stronger than her conscience. From that day, I was that girl's slave."

"Who struck off your chains? Why will you persist in considering your vital experiences from the absurd point

of view of good and evil? Where is the evil of indulgence
in sensuality? One man or women is sensual, another isn't.
If anyone has a right to complain of your enslavement, it is
I. Your philandering forced upon me a long period of inactivity which was only made bearable by the opportunity
you afforded me for studying sex psychology from the life.
When my patience wore out I freed you from your bond,
you can't deny that."

"I'm coming to that. I'm in a dilemma about my work. I
don't know whether to bring in Virginia or not. It seems—
you hate my talking about right or wrong but I must—it
seems wrong to make capital out of an intimate attachment
by exposing its ugly side in a book."

"I don't understand what you mean by its ugly side,"
I answered. "The point is that your passion for her affected your life and that's what you're writing about. You
haven't even the excuse of sentiment, since you have always
denied you were in love with her."

"How could I have been, when the strongest feeling she
inspired was repulsion?'"

"It seems to me repulsion is as essential an element of
it as attraction. You finally revolted but you were her
slave."

"'Yes, I was. What I can't understand it how you managed to turn up at those critical moments."

"I've no choice in the matter; I have to obey the force."

Richard turned to and began writing feverishly.

As his work progressed, our relationship approached a
condition of equilibrium I certainly had not anticipated.
His task absorbed all his energies, and the seriousness with

which he was facing it was demonstrated less by his industry in the act of writing than in his constant references to it. Plainly, he was thinking of nothing else, or, at all events, of nothing that could not in one way or another be related to it. It was this factor especially, the relating of all forms of experience past and present to the business, making it the pivot of his interests, that provided the basis for our new understanding. For I was thus consciously able to exercise an influence which determined the ideas underlying his undertaking, if not the form in which they were cast.

At last a day came when Richard, reading aloud his work to Myrtle, said to her: "I'm afraid it's getting too long, and the worst of it is I don't know where to end."

Here I could say something.

"Why end at all? Life doesn't end, it flows on," I said.

"Do you mean I can end anywhere, arbitrarily?"

"You can end where it suits you to end. When you've said all you've got to say, stop."

"Even though it leaves the book inconclusive?"

"Life is inconclusive," I answered.

Myrtle agreed.

Richard had at last realised that the force he had so long opposed was too strong to be resisted. He doubted whether its use for his present purpose was justified, because he had already recognised that the writing of his novel was not in itself a matter of any importance and that its chief value was that it provided a channel through which the force could operate. It was at that point that he reached his closest contact with me, and through that convergence a kind of clairvoyance. He was beginning to see that his perspective had been false and that the past was only significant in so far as it afforded a background against which the present emerged, itself a jumping-off place for the future. Synchronising with his conversion to that point of view, I marked a sensible reduction in my self-assertiveness, which I attributed to my will to exist being no longer thwarted. At this juncture I determined that to be practically effective my energy must be disciplined to the use Richard was making of it, and my freedom would depend more and more upon the completeness of our synthesis. I had never expected to come to this conclusion, because I had seen in Richard nothing to lead me to anticipate the development his writing had brought about. I could now regard his work as a serious undertaking.

During the preceding stages of this history I have recorded the various policies, offensive and defensive, I was compelled to adopt by the fluctuating conditions of the strange consortium of which Destiny had made me a member. Throughout this period the urgent consideration for me was nothing less than my own survival. Up to the appearance of Myrtle, I had been compelled to avail myself of any means that lay to my hand to provide the force within me an outlet for its dynamic energy. By the law of my nature, I could only operate through Richard's personality, so that my power was confined within the narrow limits his manner of seeing, thinking and acting imposed. In consequence my spirit, chafing under a restraint it was impotent to remove, was in a constant state of rebellion, and grasped any opportunity of undermining Richard's resistance to it. He paid the penalty of the outbreaks I provoked, resulting in the continuous antagonism I have recorded. This antagonism became so deeply rooted that it persisted after Myrtle's propitiatory advent and even after the passage of time had revealed cumulative evidence of her ardent desire to reconcile us. I have shown, indeed, how often I distrusted her. But now her wisdom and integrity had borne fruit. I was at last convinced that the surest means for my self-preservation and ultimate fulfilment were to be found in the constructive co-operation of Richard and myself, a consummation that she had conceived, had laboured for with infinite patience and persistence, and which only such a love as hers could have achieved.

THE END

NOTES

The epigraph. *Richard, Myrtle and I* (New York: Alfred A. Knopf, 1926), p. 111.

Biographical Note

1. George Gissing, *A Life's Morning* (London: Smith, Elder, 1890), p. 164.
2. Stephen Hudson, "First Meetings with Katherine Mansfield," *The Cornhill Magazine*, No. 1017, Autumn, 1958, p. 209.
3. Edwin Muir, "Stephen Hudson," *The Nation*, vol. 121, Dec. 9, 1925, pp. 655-6.
4. Edwin Muir, *The Present Age* (London: The Cresset Press, 1939), p. 140.
5. Unpublished letter to S. H., Oct. 8, 1921.
6. Unpublished letter to S. H., Mar. 27, 1922.
7. Unpublished letter to S. H., Feb. 11, 1926.
8. Unpublished letter to S. H., May [n.d.], 1930.
9. Unpublished letter to S. H., Mar. 17, 1937.
10. Feb. 14, 1937.
11. *The Referee*, Mar. 23, 1930.
12. Unpublished letter to S. H., Feb. 24, 1937.
13. Mimeograph of "Stephen Hudson," talk by J. Isaacs; transmission Mar. 11, 1949, Third Program, B.B.C., p. 1.
14. Book Review Section, June 6, 1926, p. 9.
15. *Literary Digest International Book Review*, vol. iv, Sept., 1926, pp. 650-1.
16. London: E. Benn, 1932, p. 90.
17. *Ibid.*
18. The painting is owned by Violet Schiff.
19. Letter to me, Dec. 22, 1960, from R.S.B., Offices of the Council, London Stock Exchange.

20. The painting is owned by Violet Schiff.

21. Certified copy of entry of marriage, Somerset House.

22. The painting is owned by Violet Schiff.

23. The painting is in the care of Esmé Cooke.

24. Letter to me, Oct. 25, 1960, from Rose Morley.

25. Letter to me, Oct. 5, 1960, from Rose Morley.

26. Letter to me, Oct. 21, 1960, from Graham Stainforth.

27. Letter to me, Sept. 17, 1960, from Graham Stainforth.

28. David Newsome, *A History of Wellington College, 1859-1959* (London: John Murray, 1959), *passim;* and R. St. C. Talboys, *A Victorian School* (Oxford: Basil Blackwell, 1943), *passim.*

29. Letter to me, Nov. 9, 1960, from R. E. Clifford, University Registry, Oxford.

30. *Polk's Dental Register* for 1893.

31. Copy of Register, certified by the Dean and Rector of St. Luke's Cathedral, the Very Reverend F. T. Nock, Oct. 22, 1960.

32. The Registrar of the Day, Somerset House.

33. Osbert Sitwell, *Noble Essences* (Boston: Little, Brown, 1950), p. 146.

34. Rom Landau, *Ignace Paderewski* (New York: Thomas Y. Crowell, 1934), *passim;* and George R. Marek, *Puccini* (New York: Simon and Schuster, 1951), *passim.*

35. I have the highly treasured recording of her singing "Das Haidekind," "Tout Passe," and "L'Ora e Tarda," the last two by her teacher, Tosti.

36. Osbert Sitwell, *op. cit.,* pp. 158-60.

37. Mosco Carner, *Puccini, A Critical Biography* (London: G. Duckworth, 1958), *passim;* and George R. Marek, *op. cit., passim.*

38. Certified copy of marriage register, Somerset House.

39. Miron Grindea, "In Search of our Proust,'" *Adam,* No. 260, 1957, p. 9.

40. Violet Schiff, "Proust Meets Joyce," *Adam,* No. 260, 1957, pp. 64-5.

41. Stephen Hudson, "First Meetings with Katherine Mansfield," *Cornhill Magazine,* No. 1017, Autumn, 1958, pp. 202-12.

42. *An Autobiography* (London: Hogarth Press, 1954), pp. 226-7.

43. Miron Grindea, *op. cit.*, p. 7.

44. William Rothenstein, *Since Fifty, Men and Memoirs 1922-1938* (New York: Macmillan, 1944), p. 136.

45. J. Isaacs, *op. cit.*, p. 3.

46. This volume is owned by Esmé Cooke.

CRITICAL ESSAY

1. *Richard Kurt* (New York: Alfred A. Knopf, 1920), p. 202.

2. *Ibid.*, p. 110.

3. *Ibid.*, p. 115.

4. *Ibid.*, p. 238.

5. *Ibid.*, p. 292.

6. *Ibid.*, p. 228.

7. *Elinor Colhouse* (London: A. Constable, 1921), p. 117.

8. *Ibid.*, p. 159.

9. Letter to me from the Very Reverend F. T. Nock, Oct. 22, 1960.

10. *Prince Hempseed* (London: A. Constable, 1923), p. 224.

11. *Tony* (London: A. Constable, 1924), p. 28.

12. *Ibid.*, p. 180.

13. *Ibid.*, p. 184.

14. *Ibid.*, pp. 113-4.

15. *Ibid.*, p. 85.

16. *Ibid.*, p. 69.

17. *Eton School Register, 1883-1889*, p. 78.

18. Certified copy of death entry, Somerset House.

19. Letter to me, Sept. 17, 1960, from Graham Stainforth.

20. *Richard, Myrtle and I* (New York: Alfred A. Knopf, 1926), p. 180.

21. *Myrtle* (New York: Alfred A. Knopf, 1925), p. 85.

22. *Ibid.*, p. 60.

23. *Ibid.*, p. 108.

24. *Ibid.*, p. 132.

25. *Ibid.*, p. 144.

26. *Ibid.*, p. 155.

27. *Ibid.*, pp. 163-4.

28. *Ibid.*, p. 183.

29. *Ibid.*, pp. 115-6.

30. *Ibid.*, p. 138.

31. *Ibid.*, p. 41.

32. *Ibid.*, p. 62.

33. *Ibid.*, p. 191.

34. *Ibid.*, p. 58.

35. *Richard, Myrtle and I* (New York: Alfred A. Knopf, 1926), p. 236.

36. *Ibid.*, p. 104.

37. *Ibid.*, p. 4.

38. *Ibid.*, pp. 203-5.

39. *Ibid.*, pp. 95-6.

40. Mimeograph of "Stephen Hudson," talk by J. Isaacs, Mar. 11, 1949, Third Program, B.B.C., pp. 7-8.

41. *The Other Side* (London: The Cresset Press, 1937), p. 153.

42. *Ibid.*, p. 116.

43. *Ibid.*, p. 34.

44. *Poor's Manual of Railroads, 1887:* Alabama and Great Southern, pp. 663-4; Cincinnati, New Orleans and Texas Pacific, pp. 668-9; New Orleans and Northeastern, pp. 702-3; Vicksburg and Meridian, pp. 709-10; Vicksburg, Shreveport and Pacific, p. 711. *Poor's Manual, 1888*, pp. 728-9.

45. *Elinor Colhouse* (London: Martin Secker, 1921), pp. 117-19.

46. *Tony* (London: A. Constable, 1924), p. 17.

47. *The Other Side*, pp. 40-1.

48. *Prince Hempseed*, p. 247.

49. The book is now owned by Esmé Cooke.

50. *Richard, Myrtle and I*, p. 224.

51. *Ibid.*, p. 235.

52. Alexander S. C. Deans, *The Bee Keepers Encyclopedia* (Kingswood, Surrey: A. G. Elliot, 1949), p. 14.